CROSSWORDS WORD SEARCHES
LOGIC PUZZLES & SURPRISES!

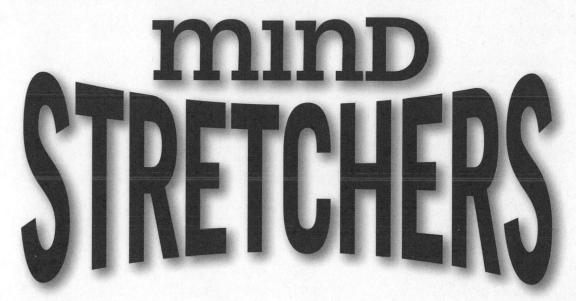

mind
STRETCHERS

PURPLE EDITION

EDITED BY STANLEY NEWMAN

Reader's Digest

The Reader's Digest Association, Inc.
Pleasantville, NY / Montreal

Project Staff

EDITORS
Neil Wertheimer, Sandy Fein

PUZZLE EDITOR
Stanley Newman

PRINCIPAL PUZZLE AUTHORS
George Bredehorn, Stanley
Newman, Dave Phillips,
Peter Ritmeester

SERIES ART DIRECTOR
Rich Kershner

DESIGNERS
Tara Long, Erick Swindell

ILLUSTRATIONS
©Norm Bendel

COPY EDITOR
Diane Aronson

Reader's Digest Home & Health Books

**PRESIDENT, HOME & GARDEN
AND HEALTH & WELLNESS**
Alyce Alston

EDITOR IN CHIEF
Neil Wertheimer

CREATIVE DIRECTOR
Michele Laseau

EXECUTIVE MANAGING EDITOR
Donna Ruvituso

**ASSOCIATE DIRECTOR,
NORTH AMERICA PREPRESS**
Douglas A. Croll

MANUFACTURING MANAGER
John L. Cassidy

MARKETING DIRECTOR
Dawn Nelson

The Reader's Digest Association, Inc.

**PRESIDENT AND
CHIEF EXECUTIVE OFFICER**
Mary Berner

**PRESIDENT,
CONSUMER MARKETING**
Dawn Zier

**VICE PRESIDENT,
CONSUMER MARKETING**
Kathryn Bennett

ISBN 978-0-7621-0785-8

Address any comments about *Mind Stretchers*, *Purple Edition* to:

The Reader's Digest Association, Inc.
Editor in Chief, Books
Reader's Digest Road
Pleasantville, NY 10570-7000

To order copies of this or other editions of the *Mind Stretchers* book series,
call 1-800-846-2100.

Visit our online store at **rdstore.com**

For many more fun games and puzzles, visit www.rd.com/games.

Printed in the United States of America

1 3 5 7 9 10 8 6 4 2

US 4967/L-5

Contents

Dear Puzzler,

For the vast majority of participants, puzzles are simply a fun and healthy diversion. But as with any pastime, there are those who take puzzles seriously. *Very* seriously.

And for such people, there is the World Puzzle Championship.

The WPC is held annually in cities around the world, and is one of the few professional events to get me out from behind my desk, where I spend most days working on new brain challenges. Since the early 1990s, as a member of the U.S. delegation to the WPC, I've been to such far-flung destinations as Istanbul, Helsinki, and Rio de Janeiro—and also here in my backyard in suburban New York City. Though I've never competed in a WPC, I've served as captain of Canadian and multination teams.

The WPC is organized by the World Puzzle Federation, a global association of puzzle organizations with nearly 50 member nations. The goals of the federation are "to provide the means for an international exchange of puzzle ideas, stimulate innovations in the field of puzzles, and to foster friendship among puzzle enthusiasts worldwide." Since 2006, the federation has also administered an annual World Sudoku Championship.

The American organization representing the WPF is headed by my friend and colleague Will Shortz, puzzle editor of *The New York Times*. Each year, members of Team USA are chosen by an online U.S. Puzzle Championship.

What are the puzzles like? Since, by WPF rules, the puzzles must be language- and culture-neutral, you won't see any crosswords. Because some nations don't use the Roman alphabet, most puzzles don't even require knowledge of the alphabet.

That doesn't mean that the puzzle selection ever seems limited in any way. Far from it! The puzzle roster presented by the WPC host country each year is remarkable for its variety and innovation. It includes arithmetic, logic and geometric puzzles; picture puzzles; jigsaw puzzles; and mechanical puzzles.

And yes, quite a few of the puzzle types in Mind Stretchers, such as Sudoku, Star Search, and Find the Ships, are used in the WPC. Not coincidentally, Peter Ritmeester, whom I first met at a WPC and who created many of the puzzles in this book, just happens to be the General Secretary of the World Puzzle Federation. But don't worry—the logic puzzles here are much easier than the toughies faced by WPC competitors!

If you'd like to know more about international puzzling and its history, as well as try some sample competition puzzles for yourself, visit these Web sites:

• World Puzzle Federation: www.worldpuzzle.org

• Team USA: wpc.puzzles.com

Until then, enjoy the puzzles on the pages ahead. We're sure you'll find them fun, challenging, and great for your brain power!

Stanley Newman
Mind Stretchers Puzzle Editor

■ Foreword

Meet the Puzzles!

Mind Stretchers is filled with a delightful mix of classic and new puzzle types. To help you get started, here are instructions, tips, and examples for each.

WORD GAMES

Crossword Puzzles

Edited by Stanley Newman

Crosswords are arguably America's most popular puzzles. As presented in this book, the one- and two-star puzzles test your ability to solve straightforward clues to everyday words. "More-star" puzzles have a somewhat broader vocabulary, but most of the added challenge in these comes from less obvious and trickier clues. These days, you'll be glad to know, uninteresting obscurities such as "Genus of fruit flies" and "Famed seventeenth-century soprano" don't appear in crosswords anymore.

Our 60 crosswords were authored by more than a dozen different puzzle makers, all nationally known for their skill and creativity.

Clueless Crosswords

by George Bredehorn

A unique crossword variation invented by George, these 7-by-7 grids primarily test your vocabulary and reasoning skills. There is one simple task: Complete the crossword with common uncapitalized seven-letter words, based entirely on the letters already filled in for you.

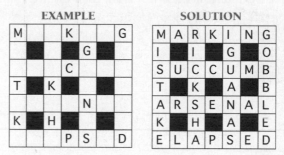

Hints: Focusing on the last letter of a word, when given, often helps. For example, a last letter of G often suggests that IN are the previous two letters. When the solutions aren't coming quickly, focus on the shared spaces that are blank—you can often figure out whether it has to be a vowel or a consonant, helping you solve both words that cross it.

Split Decisions

by George Bredehorn

Crossword puzzle lovers also enjoy this variation. Once again, no clues are provided except within the diagram. Each answer consists of two words whose spellings are the same, except for two consecutive letters. For each pair of words, the two sets of different letters are already filled in for you. All answers are common words; no phrases or hyphenated or capitalized words are used. Certain missing words may have more than one possible solution, but there is only one solution for each word that will correctly link up with all the other words.

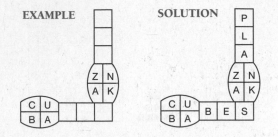

Hints: *Start with the shorter (three- and four-letter) words, because there will be fewer possibilities that spell words. In each puzzle, there will always be a few such word pairs that have only one solution. You may have to search a little to find them, since they may be anywhere in the grid, but it's always a good idea to fill in the answers to these first.*

Triad Split Decisions

by George Bredehorn

This puzzle is solved the same way as Split Decisions, except you are given three letters for each word instead of two.

Word Searches

Kids love 'em, and so do grownups, making word searches perhaps the most widely appealing puzzle type. In a word search, the challenge is to find hidden words within a grid of letters. In the typical puzzle, words can be found in vertical columns, horizontal rows, or along diagonals, with the letters of the words running either forward or backward. Usually, a list of words to search for is given to you. But to make word searches harder, puzzle writers

ANSWERS!

Answers to all the puzzles are found beginning on page 233, and are organized by the page number on which the puzzle appears.

sometimes just point you in the right direction, such as telling you to find 25 foods. Other twists include allowing words to take right turns, or leaving letters out of the grid.

Hints: *One of the most reliable and efficient searching methods is to scan each row from top to bottom for the first letter of the word. So if you are looking for "violin" you would look for the letter "v." When you find one, look at all the letters that surround it for the second letter of the word (in this case, "i"). Each time you find a correct two-letter combination (in this case, "vi"), you then scan either for the correct three-letter combination ("vio") or the whole word.*

NUMBER GAMES

Sudoku

by Peter Ritmeester

Sudoku puzzles have become massively popular in the past few years, thanks to their simplicity and test of pure reasoning. The basic Sudoku puzzle is a 9-by-9 square grid, split into 9 square regions, each containing 9 cells. Each puzzle starts off with roughly 20 to 35 of the squares filled in with the numbers 1 to 9. There is just one rule: Fill in the rest of the squares

EXAMPLE

		8	2	4			9	1
7		4	9	8		6		2
1			5		3			
	9	1		7		5	8	4
2	8		4			1		3
		3			2			
8	1	6						
	4	3		2	5		1	
	7	2						8

SOLUTION

6	5	8	2	4	7	3	9	1
7	3	4	9	8	1	6	5	2
1	2	9	5	6	3	8	4	7
3	9	1	6	7	2	5	8	4
2	8	7	4	5	9	1	6	3
4	6	5	3	1	8	2	7	9
8	1	6	7	3	4	9	2	5
9	4	3	8	2	5	7	1	6
5	7	2	1	9	6	4	3	8

with the numbers 1 to 9 so that no number appears twice in any row, column, or region.

Hints: Use the numbers provided to rule out where else the same number can appear. For example, if there is a 1 in a cell, a 1 cannot appear in the same row, column, or region. By scanning all the cells that the various 1 values rule out, you often can find where the remaining 1 values must go.

Hyper-Sudoku

by Peter Ritmeester

Peter is the inventor of this unique Sudoku variation. In addition to the numbers 1 to 9 appearing in each row and column, Hyper-Sudoku also has four 3-by-3 regions to work with, indicated by gray shading.

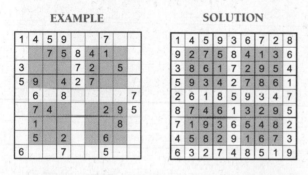

LOGIC PUZZLES

Find the Ships

by Peter Ritmeester

If you love playing the board game Battleship, you'll enjoy this pencil-and-paper variation! In each puzzle, a group of ships of varying sizes is provided on the right. Your job: Properly place the ships in the grid. A handful of ship "parts" are put on the board to get you started. The placement rules:

1. Ships must be oriented horizontally or vertically. No diagonals!

2. A ship can't go in a square with wavy lines; that indicates water.

3. The numbers on the left and bottom of the grid tell you how many squares in that row or column contain part of ships.

4. No two ships can touch each other, even diagonally.

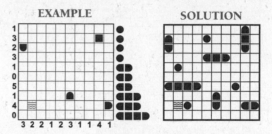

Hints: The solving process involves both finding those squares where a ship must go and eliminating those squares where a ship cannot go. The numbers provided should give you a head start with the latter, the number 0 clearly implying that every square in that row or column can be eliminated. If you know that a square will be occupied by a ship, but don't yet know what kind of ship, mark that square, then cross out all the squares that are diagonal to it—all of these must contain water.

ABC

by Peter Ritmeester

This innovative new puzzle challenges your logic much in the way a Sudoku puzzle does. Each row and column in an ABC puzzle contains exactly one A, one B, and one C, plus one blank (or two, in harder puzzles). Your task is to figure out where the three letters go in each row. The clues outside the puzzle frame tell you the first letter encountered when moving in the direction of an arrow.

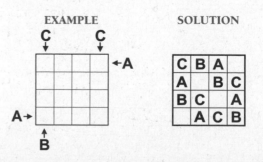

Hints: *If a clue says a letter is first in a row or column, don't assume that it must go in the first square. It could go in either of the first two squares (or first three, in the harder puzzles). A good way to start is to look for where column and row clues intersect (for example, when two clues look like they are pointing at the same square). These intersecting clues often give you the most information about where the first letter of a row or column must go. At times, it's also possible to figure out where a certain letter goes by eliminating every other square as a possibility for that letter in a particular row or column.*

Circular Reasoning

by Peter Ritmeester
Lovers of mazes will enjoy these challenges. Your task: Connect all of the circles by drawing a single line through every square of the diagram. But there are a few rules:

1. All right-angle turns must alternate between boxes containing a circle and boxes without a circle.

2. You must make a right-angle turn out of every square that contains a circle.

3. The line enters every square exactly once.

4. The line must end in the square that it began.

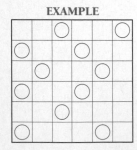
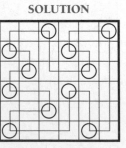

EXAMPLE   SOLUTION

Hint: *Look for a corner with no circle in it. Since the line must make a right-angle turn in this square, according to the above rules, both sides of the line must continue straight until reaching a circle, then make a right-angle turn out of that square.*

Islands

by Peter Ritmeester
Your task: Shade in some of the blank squares (as "water"), so that each remaining white box is part of an island. Here are the rules:

1. Each island will contain exactly one numbered square, indicating how many squares that island contains.

2. Each island is separated from the other islands by water but may touch other islands diagonally.

3. All water is connected.

4. There are no 2-by-2 regions of water.

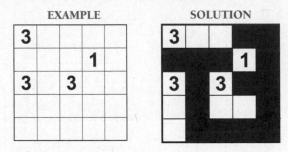

EXAMPLE   SOLUTION

Hints: *The most useful squares are those with 1 in them. Since an island with a "1" contains only that one square, you can black in every square adjacent to it. If you know three connected right-angle squares are water, by rule #4 above, the fourth square in the 2-by-2 region must be part of an island.*

Star Search

by Peter Ritmeester
Another fun game in the same style of Minesweeper. Your task: find the stars that are hidden among the blank squares. The numbered squares indicate how many stars are hidden in squares adjacent to them (including diagonally). There is never more than one star in any square.

Hint: *If, for example, a 3 is surrounded by four empty squares, but two of those squares are adja-*

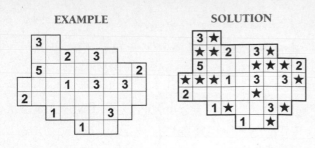

EXAMPLE   SOLUTION

cent to the same square with a 1, the other two empty squares around the 3 must contain stars.

123

by Peter Ritmeester

Each grid in this puzzle has pieces that look like dominoes. You must fill in the blank squares so that each "domino" contains one each of the numbers 1, 2, and 3, according to these two rules:

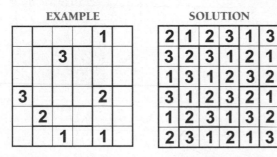

EXAMPLE   SOLUTION

1. No two adjacent squares, horizontally or vertically, can have the same number.

2. Each completed row and column of the diagram will have an equal number of 1s, 2s, and 3s.

Hints: Look first for any blank square that is adjacent to two different numbers. By rule 1 above, the "missing" number of 1-2-3 must go in that blank square. Rule 2 becomes important to use later in the solving process., For example, knowing that a 9-by-9 diagram must have three 1s, three 2s, and three 3s in each row and column allows you to use the process of elimination to deduce what blank squares in nearly filled rows and columns must be.

Throughout *Mind Stretchers* you will find unique mazes, visual conundrums, and other colorful challenges, each developed by maze master Dave Phillips. Each comes under a new name and has unique instructions. Our best advice? Patience and perseverance. Your eyes will need time to unravel the visual secrets.

In addition, you will also discover these visual puzzles:

Line Drawings

by George Bredehorn

George loves to create never-before-seen puzzle types, and here is another unique Bredehorn game. Each Line Drawing puzzle is different in its design, but the task is the same: Figure out where to place the prescribed number of lines to partition the space in the instructed way.

Hint: Use a pencil and a straightedge as you work. Some lines come very close to the items within the region, so being straight and accurate with your line-drawing is crucial.

One-Way Streets

by Peter Ritmeester

Another fun variation on the maze. The diagram represents a pattern of streets. A and B are parking spaces, and the black squares are stores. Find a route that starts at A, passes through all the stores exactly once, and ends at B. (Harder puzzles use P's to indicate parking spaces instead of A's and B's, and don't tell you the starting and ending places.) Arrows indicate one-way traffic for that block only. No

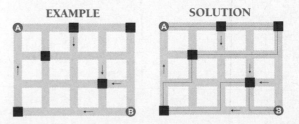

EXAMPLE   SOLUTION

block or intersection may be entered more than once.

Hints: The particular arrangement of stores and arrows will always limit the possibilities for the first store passed through from the starting point A and the last store passed through before reaching ending point B. So try to work both from the start and the end of the route. Also, the placement of an arrow on a block doesn't necessarily mean that your route will pass through that block. You can also use arrows to eliminate blocks where your path will not go.

BRAIN TEASERS

To round out the more involved puzzles are more than 150 short brain teasers, most written by our puzzle editor, Stanley Newman. Stan is famous in the puzzle world for his inventive brain games. An example of how to solve each puzzle appears in the puzzle's first occurrence (the page number is noted below). You'll find the following types scattered throughout the pages.

* Invented by and cowritten with George Bredehorn

** By George Bredehorn

But wait...there's more!

At the top of many of the pages in this book are additional brain teasers, organized into three categories:

• **QUICK!**: These tests challenge your ability to instantly calculate numbers or recall well-known facts.

• **DO YOU KNOW** ...: These more demanding questions probe the depth of your knowledge of facts and trivia.

• **HAVE YOU** ...: These reminders reveal the many things you can do each day to benefit your brain.

For the record, we have deliberately left out answers to the **QUICK!** and **DO YOU KNOW...** features. Our hope is that if you don't know an answer, you'll be intrigued enough to open a book or search the Internet for it!

Meet the Authors

STANLEY NEWMAN (puzzle editor and author) is crossword editor for *Newsday*, the major newspaper of Long Island, New York. He is the author/editor of over 125 books, including the autobiography and instructional manual *Cruciverbalism* and the best-selling *Million Word Crossword Dictionary*. Winner of the First U.S. Open Crossword Championship in 1982, he holds the world's record for the fastest completion of a *New York Times* crossword— 2 minutes, 14 seconds. Stan operates the website www.StanXwords.com and also conducts an annual Crossword University skill-building program on a luxury-liner cruise.

GEORGE BREDEHORN is a retired elementary school teacher from Wantagh, New York. His variety word games have appeared in the *New York Times* and many puzzle magazines. Every week for the past 20 years, he and his wife, Dorothy, have hosted a group of Long Island puzzlers who play some of the 80-plus games that George has invented.

DAVE PHILLIPS has designed puzzles for books, magazines, newspapers, PC games, and advertising for more 30 years. In addition, Dave is a renowned creator of walk-through mazes. Each year his corn-maze designs challenge visitors with miles of paths woven into works of art. Dave is also codeveloper of eBrainyGames.com, a website that features puzzles and games for sale.

PETER RITMEESTER is chief executive officer of PZZL.com, which produces many varieties of puzzles for newspapers and websites worldwide. Peter is also general secretary of the World Puzzle Federation. The federation organizes the annual World Puzzle Championship, which includes difficult versions of many of the types of logic puzzles that Peter has created for *Mind Stretchers*.

■ Master Class: **Vocabulary**

The Five Best Ways to Increase Your Word Power

On average, the typical American uses about 2,000 different words in a week, and in total, has about 20,000 in their vocabulary.

Is that good or bad? Who knows! It's impossible to say without a little context. So these additional numbers might help:

• Dr. Seuss' *Green Eggs and Ham*, one of the best-selling children's books of all time, uses only 50 different words.

• William Shakespeare, perhaps the most literate person of his time, used about 30,000 different words in all of his works, and he no doubt knew more than a few words that didn't make it into his plays and sonnets (for example, we don't think the phrase, "Honey, where are my knickers?" is in any of his plays).

• Experts estimate there are about 1 million English words in total. That means for every word we use or know, there are 49 we *don't* use or know!

Numbers aside, there are many compelling reasons why you should focus on building your vocabulary. The benefits include:

•You'll be able to express yourself more subtly and precisely;

• You'll understand more of what you read and hear;

• You'll be able to think better. After all, everyone does their thinking with words, and you can't think with words that you don't know;

• You'll have an enhanced ability to learn new things. As noted word expert Wilfred Funk once said, "The more words you know, the more clearly and powerfully you will think and the more ideas you will invite into your mind."

So without further ado (which is fairly close to something Shakespeare said), here are my favorite ways to build vocabulary. Couple these with the tools mentioned in the sidebar on page 13, and you'll be growing your vocabulary by leaps and bounds!

METHOD ONE:
Crossword Puzzles

You already know that learning more words is great for solving crosswords, but the reverse is equally true. The crosswords you do every day can be a wonderful springboard for increasing your vocabulary, if you take full advantage of the opportunity.

To do so, you'll need to add a second objective, besides solving, to every crossword you encounter. After you've filled in those little white boxes, review all of the puzzle's clues and answers. Mark any word you're not familiar with, any meaning of a familiar word that may be new to you, and any word you're not sure how to pronounce. Then look up in your dictionary each item you've marked and enter it in your New Word File. Include the word, its meaning and/or pronunciation, and today's date.

For an extra benefit, be sure to read the entire entry for each word you look up, including all the definitions, usage examples, if any (which will help you distinguish it from other words with similar meanings), and the etymology—the word's history. Jot down any additional information you've learned in your New Word File. This should add to your pleasure in discovering each new word as well as help you to remember it.

METHOD TWO:
Scrabble

Although Scrabble skills are different from crossword skills (knowledge of word meanings isn't necessary in Scrabble, for example), if you're like most crossword fans, you probably play Scrabble at least once in a while. To leverage your Scrabble play most effectively to learn new words, I recommend that you change the rules just a little. I know this method works, because I've played Scrabble this way for many years.

While the official rules prohibit the looking up of words, you and your playing partners should be free to consult any convenient dictionary, and to use any word that otherwise conforms to the rules (uncapitalized, unhyphenated, etc.). Not only will you learn

Vocabulary Builder's Standard Equipment

If you're serious about vocabulary improvement, here are a few things you'll need.

1. An up-to-date college dictionary

This will be your primary reference for looking up words and/or meanings that are new to you. By up-to-date, we mean published in the past five years, which you can verify on the copyright page. With the English language being added to at such a rapid rate, and new meanings of words coming into currency all the time, your college dictionary must be as new as possible.

Which college dictionary to choose? Your favorite bookstore or online bookseller offers choices from many major publishers, all of which do a good job. Beware, though, of "bargain" dictionaries from publishers you've never heard of. Chances are they're nowhere near as current as you'd expect. We suggest that, among publishers whose names you know, you pick the college dictionary with the most recent publication date.

2. A "New Word File"

You'll need this to keep a "master list" of everything you've learned. We suggest index cards and a file box to hold them, but anything similar that allows you to record and save your new words alphabetically is okay.

3. Pen and paper

The trick is to have them ready wherever you are, because you never know when or where you'll encounter a new word. Quickly jot down new words heard or seen, look them up later, and add to your New Word File.

4. An unabridged dictionary

By definition, unabridged dictionaries have many more words than college dictionaries—at least twice as many or more. At least occasionally, you're likely to come across unfamiliar words that aren't in your college dictionary, and that's when you'll need to open your unabridged. Why not just buy an unabridged instead of a college dictionary? Because of their massive size, unabridged dictionaries aren't updated very often.

many new words that you might not come across any other way, but your scores will no doubt be higher as well—a nice side benefit! Be sure to add all words that are new to you into your New Word File.

You might also try playing "Scrabble Solitaire," with no opponent at all, with the dual objectives of learning new words and reaching the highest possible score.

METHOD THREE:
Everyday Reading

The one drawback of Scrabble and Crossword puzzles is that the words you learn from them won't necessarily be all that useful. That's why it's important for your everyday reading to be an ongoing source of new words for you.

So follow a basic rule: As you read, write down any word for which you don't know the meaning. Later on, look it up and add to your New Word File.

Are the magazines, newspapers, and books that you're reading regularly too "easy" for your vocabulary-building program? There's an easy way to find out. For the next week, write down on a sheet of paper all the new words you come across from your regular reading. If that sheet is blank at the end of the week, or has just a word or two on it, don't fret. It just means that, like many other people, you're in a "comfort zone" with your reading that you'll need to start reaching beyond.

Your first step should be an "upgrade" of your magazine reading, to include publications with a higher-level vocabulary. They can be magazines on topics you aren't expert in, or the magazines famous for lengthy narrative writing (such as the *Atlantic Monthly*, *Vanity Fair*, or *The New Yorker*). Then, look for books in subjects you've always wanted to learn more about. Such books are bound to have lots of words that will be new to you.

Your best ally for this part of your program is your local public library. It's conveniently located, and it won't cost you a nickel. Your library almost certainly has subscriptions to all the magazines mentioned above. Whether you're interested in archaeology, airplanes, or African art, there will be books waiting for you on the library shelves. We also suggest that you talk to your friendly neighborhood librarian, who will be glad to make additional recommendations.

METHOD FOUR:
"New Word" products

You've probably seen a wide variety of "Page a Day" tear-off calendars in your local bookstore. Several publishers have "New Word a Day" calendars, which you may find useful in your vocabulary-building. But try to sneak a peek at the words presented on the calendar before you purchase it. If you already know most of the words, that calendar's not for you.

Of course, if you have an unabridged dictionary, you won't need a calendar to get your new-word-a-day. Simply open your dictionary to a page at random and look for a new, interesting word to add to your list. There's bound to be at least one on every page.

Your humble puzzle editor learns new words this way all the time. My latest discovery, from a random page of the *Random House Unabridged*, is "numinous," pronounced as in "luminous." It means "spiritual or supernatural," and is derived from "numen," a divine power or spirit.

METHOD FIVE:
The Computer

With a personal computer and the Internet, you've got zillions of free vocabulary-building resources available to you. If you've been waiting for the right reason to become computer-literate, you've got it now. Most public libraries give free Internet access to their patrons, and many offer free "Computer 101" classes as well. You can become comfortable with using a computer before you buy one for your home.

There's no doubt that Internet access is a dream come true for the intellectually curious, because you're only a couple of seconds and a couple of mouse clicks away from any possible topic you'd like to learn more about. So, if you've been holding back, please consider taking the "PC plunge." Your brain will thank you. Here are just a few of our favorite vocabulary resources on the World Wide Web:

• *www.spellingbee.com:* This official Web site of the venerable National Spelling Bee has a "Study Zone" section that includes a self-study course, its "Consolidated Word List" (from which most words used in the contests are taken), and much more.

• *"Word a day" e-mails:* Numerous word-related Web sites offer to e-mail you a new word every day. We especially like www.dictionary.com and www.wordsmith.org, but there are many more.

• *www.freerice.com:* This unique charity Web site features an interactive multiple-choice vocabulary quiz that deduces your skill level from words that you know, then gradually presents more difficult words you're not likely to know. For each word you correctly identify, 20 grains of rice are donated through the United Nations to help fight world hunger.

Or discover your own favorites. Enter the phrase "improve your vocabulary" at a search engine like google.com and you'll be presented with a directory of many thousands of Web pages that contain it. Or search "Word a day e-mail" and you'll get all kinds of services that provide a daily vocabulary challenge to your e-mail box.

A Few Final Words

To make sure you retain the new words you learn, be sure to review your New Word File regularly. It's great to do this with a friend or relative, who you might get to quiz you once in a while. Perhaps you can even convince your friend to build a New Word File of his or her own, and you can quiz each other.

By all means, try to work some of your new words into your everyday conversation, but be careful. Don't make the mistake of using "ten-dollar words" all the time. You want to make yourself sound smarter, but don't make others scratch their heads because they don't understand what you're trying to say.

It will take time and effort to increase your vocabulary in a meaningful way, so please be patient. The benefits are more than worth it. I know it will give you a great sense of accomplishment when you recognize a word you've recently learned. So by all means, reward yourself each time you do. Take an Oreo out of the cupboard, pat yourself on the back, whatever.

Have fun, and good luck!

—Stanley Newman

★ Take the Cake by Gail Grabowski

ACROSS

1 __ of Riley (ease)
5 Cincinnati baseballers
9 Rotini or rigatoni
14 Sandwich cookie
15 Director Kazan
16 Speedy
17 Keyboard symbol above "3"
19 Wear away
20 Conclusion
21 Henhouse perch
22 Ice-cream holders
23 Work in the mailroom
24 Baker's topping
26 Perfume feature
28 Southwest art center
29 Air-quality org.
32 Seacoast
33 Cruel character
34 Crashing sound
35 Spat
36 Bandleader's stick
38 Have the courage
39 Comic-strip bark
40 Manuscript mailing enclosure: Abbr.
41 Interrupt, on the dance floor
42 Map line: Abbr.
43 Avoid an F
44 Draggy feeling, with "the"
45 Clean the blackboard
47 Banister
48 Difficult problem
50 Back of a ship
52 Roads: Abbr.
55 Theater seater
56 Infield position
58 "__ Were the Days"
59 Pennsylvania port
60 Brazil neighbor
61 Recorded
62 Boring
63 Very impressed

DOWN

1 Easy stride
2 Remove wrinkles
3 Long-running quarrel
4 Very long time
5 Vacation spot
6 Poet T.S.
7 Uses a shovel
8 Capital of Chile
9 Exact
10 Spelling or Burr
11 Patient's washup
12 Ocean motion
13 Fruity drinks
18 Male bee
23 Feudal worker
25 Crop on stalks
26 T or polo
27 Small eatery
28 Lugs around
30 Eiffel Tower city
31 Prayer's end
32 Movie rating symbol
36 Lambs' sounds
37 Levied, as taxes
38 Twofold
40 Practiced some punches
41 Mr. Eastwood
44 Winemaker's container
46 Singer Della
47 Stop a squeak again
48 Short golf stroke
49 Workplace safety group: Abbr.
51 Drive-__ window
52 Slow-cooked meal
53 Pulled apart
54 Potato, slangily
57 Fitness center

★ Bar Tending

Which bar was laid down in the middle of the pile, having the same number of bars below it as above it?

COUNTDOWN

Inserting plus signs and minus signs, as many as necessary, in between the digits from 9 to 1 below, create a series of additions and subtractions whose final answer is 5. Any digits without a sign between them are to be grouped together as a single number.

Example: 9 8 + 7 6 - 5 4 - 3 + 2 1 = 138

| 9 | 8 | 7 | 6 | 5 | 4 | 3 | 2 | 1 | = | 5 |

★ Sweet Stuff

Find the 18 words or phrases for sweet foods that are hidden in the diagram either across, down, or diagonally. Answers include two two-word phrases and three plurals ending in S.

```
M S H E R B E T S J T I
E D C M N I S T J A T T
R S A H C I U Y G A O E
I J Y I O N P U R F H L
N M N R H C O E F U S F
G G A G Y N O E L B P I
U A U E I P E L P P A R
E O F Y R S M E A S P T
D U U C L C A K J T L G
F U D G A L E A A R E R
S U G A R K E C J A T T
J Y E N O H O J I T F P
```

INITIAL REACTION

The "equation" below contains the initials of words that will make it correct, forming a numerical fact. Solve the equation by supplying the missing words. Example: 60 = M. in an H. (Minutes in an Hour)

32 = O. in a Q. _____

★ Sudoku

Fill in the blank boxes so that every row, column, and 3x3 box contains all of the numbers 1 to 9.

	8	9	6		7		3	
		1						
7	3			9	2	4	8	
4	6	3	5	2				
9	5	7				6		3
			7	6	3	9	4	5
	9							
		4		8		7	5	2
8		6		5	4			9

MIXAGRAMS

Each line contains a five-letter word and a four-letter word that have been mixed together (the order of the letters in each word has not been changed). Unmix the two words on each line and write them in the spaces provided. When you're done, find a two-part answer to the clue by reading down the letter columns in the answers. Example: D A R I U N V E T = DRIVE + AUNT

CLUE: G.I.'s delight

C A R M I E C E L = _ _ _ _ _ + _ _ _ _

C O H E A T A H L = _ _ _ _ _ + _ _ _ _

S C A L P I M E L = _ _ _ _ _ + _ _ _ _

B I F L O G L E D = _ _ _ _ _ + _ _ _ _

★ On Foot by Shirley Soloway

ACROSS

1 Anwar of Egypt
6 Limerick, e.g.
10 Nautical pole
14 Occupied
15 Thomas __ Edison
16 Curve of the foot
17 Ceiling painter's need
19 __ & *Stitch* (Disney film)
20 Publicity photos
21 Low-tech counting device
23 Business leader: Abbr.
24 Video-game emporium
26 Church bench
29 Overhauled tire
31 Homburg, for one
34 Assumed name
36 Elevator inventor
37 Take the bus
38 Broadway prize
39 Tractor-trailer
40 Similar
41 Rotate
42 Org.
43 Having a high incline
44 Japanese coin
45 Leon of Russia
47 Total
48 Military command
50 "This __ test ..."
52 Colin or Dick
54 Menu listing
57 Persia, today
58 In a shrill way
62 Building extensions
63 Ireland nickname
64 City south of Fort Lauderdale
65 Wee 'un
66 Assistant
67 Attack

DOWN

1 Bro's sib
2 Picnic pests
3 Song for two
4 Savory jelly
5 Bank employees
6 Shoulder shapers
7 Ancient
8 December 24 or 31
9 Rattlelike instruments
10 Lunch order
11 Wallet lighteners
12 Rights grp.
13 Greek consonants
18 Lotion ingredient
22 Rotten
24 Performer, fancily
25 Has control
26 Scam victim
27 Skip the ceremony
28 Squash the competition
30 Sculpture subjects
32 Farewell, in France
33 TV news hour
35 Writer Rand
37 Disloyal one
42 Shrinking Asian water
43 Logical procedures
45 __ Aviv
46 Considerate
49 All wound up
51 Golfer Palmer's nickname
52 Painter Mondrian
53 Paris airport
54 German article
55 State: Fr.
56 Sailor's saint
59 Numerical prefix
60 Disencumber
61 __ and yang

★ Circular Reasoning

Connect all of the circles by drawing a single continuous line through every square of the diagram. All right-angle turns of your line must alternate between boxes containing a circle and boxes not containing a circle. You must make a right-angle turn out of every square that contains a circle. Your line must end in the same square that it begins, and it cannot enter any square more than once.

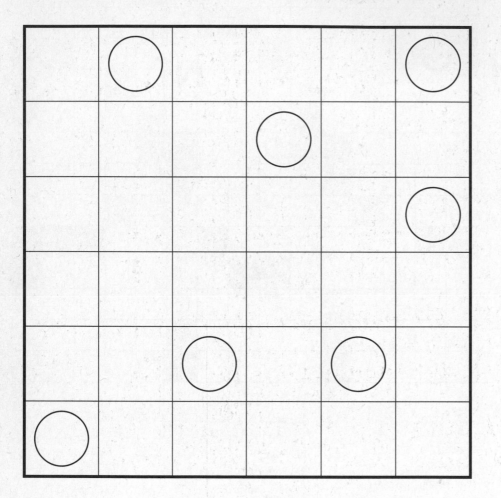

ADDITION SWITCH

Switch the positions of two of the digits in the incorrect sum at right, to get a correct sum.
Example: 955+264 = 411. Switch the second 1 in 411 with the 9 in 955 to get: 155+264 = 419

$$\begin{array}{r} 420 \\ +187 \\ \hline 967 \end{array}$$

★★ Line Drawing

Draw three straight lines, each from one edge of the square to another edge, so that the letters in each of the six regions spell a number.

THREE OF A KIND

Find the three hidden words in the sentence that, read in order, go together in some way.
Example: I sold Norma new screwdrivers (answer: "old man river").

We do hope some stores will have a sale on kitchenware.

★ Security Checks

Find these security-conscious words that are hidden in the diagram either across, down, or diagonally.

```
C K E E P O U Q D J V D
H R M O E S H U T O U O
A D T Y D E V I C E G I
I S E P A D L O C K S S
N T E R C E S E C R T T
S O F V I S H U T O U T
R U G T R W M T Z O F G
B E O C R R D S P E A E
D E D C A K F E N C R R
D R A L B S E C B T A A
A O A C I K E U X R L W
U R G U O G W R C E A E
G O H L G N H I R L R B
Y R T N E O N T P A B E
S K C E H C S Y C C T N
```

ALARM
ALERTS
BARBED WIRE
BARRICADE
BEACON
BEWARE
CCTV
CHAINS
CHECKS
DEVICE
DOGS
FENCE
GUARD
KEEP OUT
NO ENTRY
PADLOCKS
RED LIGHT
SECRET
SECURITY
SHUT OUT
STOP

TONGUE TWISTER

From what language are all of these words derived:

AVALANCHE, VINTAGE, RESTAURANT, and FRONTIER?

A) Japanese B) Dutch C) French D) Scottish

★ City Structures by Gail Grabowski

ACROSS

1 Celebrity
5 "Cut it out!"
9 Circle or square
14 Havana's home
15 Domesticated
16 A tad too inquisitive
17 Considerably
18 Region
19 More than sufficient
20 Land along the Mississippi
22 Annoying individuals
23 Foot-operated lever
24 Initiate a duel
26 Apartment fee
29 Book of maps
32 NASA concern
36 "I dropped it!"
38 Choir voice
40 Curved entryway
41 South American mountains
42 Guided vacation
43 Lima's locale
44 Rise in the sky
45 Kids with curfews
46 Birdcage feature
48 Community gym site
50 Gourmet cook
52 Up in the air
56 Hiding place
59 Conservative group
63 Bring forth
64 Civil unrest
65 Overture follower
66 "Absolutely not!"
67 Use a phone
68 Feels regret
69 Deuce beaters
70 Author __ Stanley Gardner
71 Manager's aide: Abbr.

DOWN

1 Sign of a past injury
2 Dutch flower
3 Superior to
4 Evaluated, as a movie
5 Stallion's home
6 Fictional plantation
7 Sign of the future
8 Mountain tops
9 Get short with
10 Where the catcher squats
11 Vile vipers
12 Animal skin
13 Facial features
21 Hard to find
25 Scottish miss
27 Forbidden thing
28 NBC morning show
30 Lotion additive
31 Astound
32 Patsy
33 Get ready, for short
34 Land measure
35 Beer-bottle opener, slangily
37 Salon wave
39 Hospital sites: Abbr.
41 Tennis great Arthur
45 Locker room powder
47 One-word toast
49 Royal residence
51 Strength
53 Scarlett of fiction
54 Adjust a camera
55 Carries around
56 Copper-coated coin
57 State with confidence
58 Small bay
60 Tall-tale teller
61 Raggedy Ann, e.g.
62 Shopping aid

★ Islands

Shade in some of the white squares in the diagram with "water," so that each remaining white box is part of an island. Each island will contain exactly one numbered square, indicating how many squares that island contains. Each island is separated from the other islands by water but may touch other islands diagonally. All water is connected, but there are no 2x2 regions of water in the diagram.

				1
		1		
3			2	
	1			

AND SO ON

Unscramble the letters in the phrase DINGY HAT, to form two words that are part of a common phrase that has the word AND between them. Example: The letters in LEATHER HAY can be rearranged to spell HALE and HEARTY.

_____ and _____

★ Turn Maze

Entering at the bottom and exiting at the top, find the shortest path through the maze, following these turn rules: You must turn right on red squares, turn left on blue squares, and go straight through yellow squares. Your path may retrace itself and cross at intersections, but you may not reverse your direction at any point.

THREE AT A RHYME

Rearrange these letters to form three one-syllable words that rhyme.
Example: A A A B C E K S W X X = AXE, BACKS, WAX

A A A B E L M P R S T T T T

_____Abe_____   _____   _____

★ On the Job by Shirley Soloway

ACROSS

1 Church service
5 Gaudy trinket
11 Common article
14 In the matter of
15 New York lake
16 Vote in favor
17 Campfire reciter
19 Cherry seed
20 Italian isle
21 1550
22 Stockholm resident
24 Gives approval
26 Evolution advocate
27 Respond
30 Not so many
31 They convened in NYC in 2004
32 Thrill ride offerings
35 Singer Simone
38 Devastate
40 Lessen in intensity
41 Attempt
42 Teacher in Siam
43 Discourages
45 CBS logo
46 Carpenter's pin
48 Need for water
50 Cooking enticements
52 Flaming felony
54 Permissible
55 To and __
56 Make a choice
60 Choose, with "for"
61 Vodka plus orange juice
64 Prefix meaning "recent"
65 Act that precedes the headliner
66 Cairo's waterway
67 Make a goof
68 Contract certifier
69 Model Macpherson

DOWN

1 Not fem. or neut.
2 Hammett hound
3 "Quit that!"
4 The blues
5 "I __ Rhythm"
6 Foe
7 Joins, as metal
8 Fish feature
9 Summer quaff
10 Capital of Poland
11 Obsolete office machine
12 Fictional Alpine girl
13 "Thanks, I've already __"

18 "Uh-oh!"
23 Small songbirds
25 Video game parlors
26 Sahara and Gobi
27 Taj Mahal town
28 Person, place, or thing
29 Image consultant
30 Big party
33 Biblical brother
34 Sinking ship deserter
36 Votes opposite 16 Across
37 Help a hoodlum
39 Ashley Judd's mom

44 Blacksmith, at times
47 Holmes cohort
49 Like some skates
50 Sans company
51 Less green, as fruit
52 Sports site
53 Oarsman
55 Worry
57 Nefarious
58 Alcatraz unit
59 Beech or birch
62 Naval noncom: Abbr.
63 Not at all humid

★ One-Way Streets

The diagram represents a pattern of streets. A and B are parking spaces, and the black squares are stores. Find the route that starts at A, passes through all stores exactly once, and ends at B. Arrows indicate one-way traffic for that block only. No block or intersection may be entered more than once.

SOUND THINKING

We can think of two common uncapitalized words whose only consonant sounds are K, L, and G (as in "go"), in that order. How many can you think of?

_____   _____

★★ Split Decisions

In this clueless crossword puzzle, each answer consists of two words whose spellings are the same, except for the consecutive letters given. All answers are common words; no phrases or hyphenated or capitalized words are used. Some of the clues may have more than one solution, but there is only one word pair that will correctly link up with all the other word pairs.

TRANSDELETION

Delete one letter from the word MEASURING and rearrange the rest, to get a type of flower.

_____

★ Star Search

Find the stars that are hidden in some of the blank squares. The numbered squares indicate how many stars are hidden in the squares adjacent to them (including diagonally). There is never more than one star in any square.

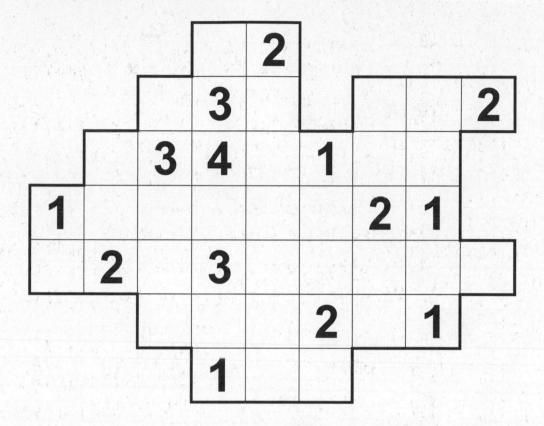

TELEPHONE TRIOS

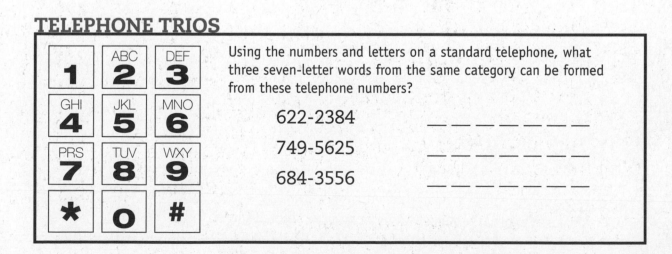

Using the numbers and letters on a standard telephone, what three seven-letter words from the same category can be formed from these telephone numbers?

622-2384   _ _ _ _ _ _ _

749-5625   _ _ _ _ _ _ _

684-3556   _ _ _ _ _ _ _

★ Deep Thinking

Find the 17 words, all at least six letters long, that all contain the letters D, E, E, and P, not necessarily in that order. Answers include six past-tense verbs ending in ED. Hint: All the words start with D.

```
D D D E P E A D L D N D
E E D E P L E T E E I E
P P S Y T P E R I S L Y
R L S P R C I U P P D O
E O E I A I L N E R L
S R V T P R E P P R E P
S E R S J A A E E A S E
M D E P S P N D D D R D
U D O E T D E P O E E P
D E P A R T E D Y T P O
E S N E P S I D R U S L
E S I P S E D O P O I E
C A E B A F P S E D D V
T T E L P E D E P O S E
I C V V D E P A D C N D
```

IN OTHER WORDS

There is only one common uncapitalized word that contains the consecutive letters SYG. What's the word?

_____

★ Simple Puzzle by Sally R. Stein

ACROSS

1 SSW or USA, for short
5 Methods
10 Plummeted
14 Insignificant
15 __ profit (do okay in business)
16 Goatee locale
17 "Simple!"
19 Princess of India
20 Gymnast Comaneci
21 RR stops
22 Help in a crime
23 Ensnare
25 Pesky insect
27 Perform on a stage
30 "Simple!"
35 Infamous Roman emperor
37 Letters on a phone
38 Little Pigs complement
39 Mets and Cardinals, for short
41 Prof's aides
43 *Love Story* author
44 Alas and __
45 Sound that asks for quiet
47 All finished
48 "Simple!"
52 Actor Beatty
53 Ruler of Kuwait
54 Bridal wear
56 Little white lies
59 Roof overhang
61 National bird
65 Polish a manuscript
66 "Simple!"
68 Bring up
69 Made more simple
70 __ of the time (occasionally)
71 Cape Canaveral org.
72 Intelligent
73 Rams' mates

DOWN

1 Congregation's response
2 Actor Lugosi
3 Born and __
4 Send payment
5 St. Helens, for one
6 Surpassed on ads, as a candidate
7 Exclamation of frustration
8 Make angry
9 Refuses to comply
10 Satisfied an itch
11 Moby Dick pursuer
12 Workday start for many
13 Make bootees
18 Wyatt of the Old West
24 Main purpose
26 PMs
27 Former UN head
28 Stringed instrument
29 Pay for a meal
31 "The __ is clear!"
32 Inert gas
33 *Family Circus* cartoonist
34 Sought long fish
36 Boston Pops, for one
40 Fat-free milk
42 One who clears snow, maybe
46 Go quickly
49 Family members
50 Alexander Bell's middle name
51 Closes a shoe
55 Run out, as a subscription
56 Type of houseplant
57 Notion
58 Preconceived notion
60 Passport stamp
62 Shine softly
63 Like some excuses
64 Potato parts
67 Banned insecticide

★ Hyper-Sudoku

Fill in the blank boxes so that every row, column, 3x3 box, *and* each of the four 3x3 gray regions contains all of the numbers 1 to 9.

			4	5				2
7	5		6		3	4	1	8
				1		5	9	3
	1	7	3			8		5
8	6		2	7	1	3		
2								7
	7							
5	2							1
1	9		7		5	2		

MIXAGRAMS

Each line contains a five-letter word and a four-letter word that have been mixed together (the order of the letters in each word has not been changed). Unmix the two words on each line and write them in the spaces provided. When you're done, find a two-part answer to the clue by reading down the letter columns in the answers.

CLUE: Shirt insert

C H U R L E S K S = _ _ _ _ _ + _ _ _ _

F U P O P I E L D = _ _ _ _ _ + _ _ _ _

F O L I A R E N K = _ _ _ _ _ + _ _ _ _

F O L A K U T E S = _ _ _ _ _ + _ _ _ _

★ Flower Power

Starting on any flower, find a path that passes through all the other flowers, ending on the flower you started with. You may not retrace your path.

BETWEENER

What four-letter word belongs between the word at left and the word at right, so that the first and second word, and the second and third word, each form a common two-word phrase?

POWER __ __ __ __ GAMES

★ 123

Fill in the diagram so that each rectangular piece has one each of the numbers 1, 2, and 3, under these rules: 1) No two adjacent squares, horizontally or vertically, can have the same number. 2) Each completed row and column of the diagram will have an equal number of 1s, 2s, and 3s.

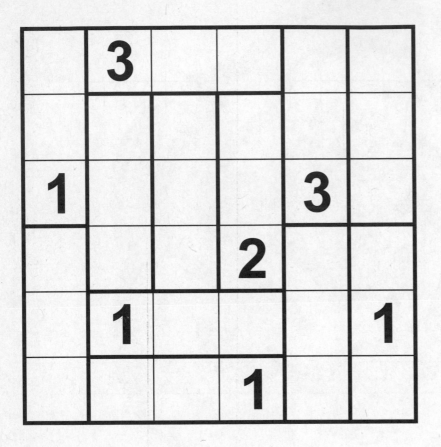

SUDOKU SUM

Without repeating any digits, complete the sum at right, by filling one digit in each of the five blanks.

$$
\begin{array}{r}
3\ \_\ 2 \\
+\ \_\ 9\ \_ \\
\hline
\_\ \_\ 6
\end{array}
$$

★ Old-Fashioned Fun by Gail Grabowski

ACROSS

1 Junk e-mail
5 Bovine baby
9 Facial features
14 Moreover
15 Opera solo
16 Emcee's opening
17 "Because I __ so!"
18 Wedding-cake layer
19 Spiral shapes
20 Children's game
23 Corp. bigwig
24 Singer Reese
25 Rib-eye, e.g.
27 Absorb, as gravy
30 Suspect's excuse
32 Show to a seat, slangily
35 High-school composition
37 Sweatshirt size
39 Chimney dust
41 Before, in poems
42 Minor mistake
43 Congress' cable channel
45 Offers at retail
48 __ Misérables
49 Wide tie
51 Open-handed hits
53 Makes a meal
55 Oklahoma city
58 Chapel words
60 Jump-rope game
64 Birth-related
66 Blunder
67 Become taller
68 Repetitive pattern
69 Poker payment
70 Golfer Player
71 Campsite leftovers
72 American Beauty, e.g.
73 Possesses

DOWN

1 Wide belt
2 Tartan pattern
3 Set __ (save)
4 Poses for photos
5 Short snoozes
6 Desertlike
7 Doesn't tell the truth
8 Taxi charges
9 Jefferson coins
10 Yoko __
11 Street game
12 Author __ Stanley Gardner
13 Mediocre
21 Lotion ingredient
22 Pilot's announcement: Abbr.
26 Goals
28 Depletes, with "up"
29 Removes the rind
31 Nastase of tennis
32 West Coast coll.
33 Slugger Sammy
34 Sidewalk game
36 Holler
38 Vinyl records
40 Filled tortilla
44 Chicken soup add-ins
46 Charge-card charge
47 Tater
50 Boxing match ender
52 Nancy's pal, in comics
54 Coffee addition
56 Milkshake insert
57 Oak nut
58 Ancient Peruvian
59 Calendar squares
61 '60s singer Sonny
62 Outdoor parking areas
63 Vacation rtes.
65 Bar beverage

★ ABC

Enter the letters A, B, and C into the diagram so that each row and column has exactly one A, one B, and one C. The letters outside the diagram indicate the first letter encountered, moving in the direction of the arrow. Keep in mind that after all the letters have been filled in, there will be one blank box in each row and column.

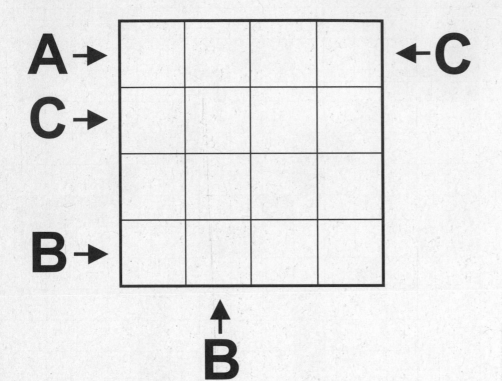

CLUELESS CROSSWORD

Complete the crossword with common uncapitalized seven-letter words, based entirely on the letters already filled in for you.

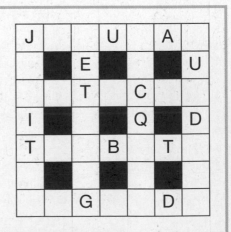

★ Find the Ships

Determine the position of the 10 ships listed to the right of the diagram. The ships may be oriented either horizontally or vertically. A square with wavy lines indicates water and will not contain a ship. The numbers at the edge of the diagram indicate how many squares in that row or column contain parts of ships. When all 10 ships are correctly placed in the diagram, no two of them will touch each other, not even diagonally.

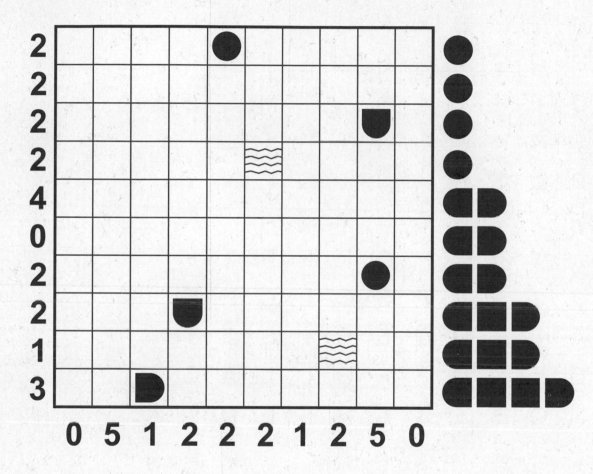

TWO-BY-FOUR

The eight letters in the word ORDINARY can be rearranged to form a pair of common four-letter words in only one way. Can you find the two words?

— — — —   — — — —

★ No Go

Find the 18 words and phrases synonymous with "stop" that are hidden in the diagram either across, down, or diagonally. One of the answers is STOP; the rest are for you to find. Answers include three two-word phrases.

```
E  R  P  N  E  D  B  R  I  P  X  E
X  S  E  E  E  X  P  U  L  L  U  P
K  H  A  S  T  G  P  S  E  N  H  R
I  D  I  E  I  A  S  I  I  M  S  E
R  S  N  K  C  G  N  T  R  T  I  T
T  R  C  I  O  K  N  I  O  E  N  I
S  F  Y  R  N  O  N  P  M  A  I  R
S  W  I  T  C  H  O  F  F  R  F  E
V  J  L  S  L  E  S  O  L  C  E  T
Q  A  I  D  U  D  E  S  I  S  Z  T
H  D  L  N  D  F  F  O  L  L  A  C
E  N  O  E  E  K  A  R  B  E  N  U
```

INITIAL REACTION

The "equation" below contains the initials of words that will make it correct, forming a numerical fact. Solve the equation by supplying the missing words.

$$12 = \text{B. on a T. (including the A. and P.S.)}$$

_____

★ Up in the Air by Sally R. Stein

ACROSS

1 Stinging insect
5 "Whatever __ Wants" (*Damn Yankees* tune)
9 Reduce drastically
14 Fictional Karenina
15 Rocks from mines
16 Number-picking game
17 Datum
18 Pesky bug
19 Dine at home
20 Very happy
23 Pen filler
24 Does the backstroke
25 Kicks out
27 Butter portion
30 Early afternoon
31 Country singer Campbell
32 Wine container
34 Astronaut Armstrong
36 Inquires
40 Wood-smoothing tool
43 Emphatic assent in Acapulco
44 Holler
45 Flying-saucer pilot
46 Below freezing
48 Droop
50 Went first
51 Arrive at
54 Pinnacles
56 It cools soda
57 Very happy
62 Rocket brake
64 Costello and Rawls
65 Region
66 "Deck the Halls," e.g.
67 Poker starter
68 Sedans and coupes
69 Battery terminal
70 Predicament
71 Necktie feature

DOWN

1 Do the laundry
2 Prefix meaning "against"
3 Unforeseen problem
4 Forest walkways
5 Enters a password
6 Placed decorations on
7 Garden-hose problems
8 Italian wine region
9 Sweater part
10 Mauna __
11 Housetop room
12 Tour of duty
13 Goose sounds
21 Got up
22 Spills the beans
26 Totally
27 One-stripe soldiers: Abbr.
28 Jai __
29 Repairs, as a driveway
31 Young cookie sellers
33 Oregano or nutmeg
35 Electrified fish
37 Leave port
38 Shin neighbor
39 Mail away
41 Sock fabric
42 Summoned via beeper
47 *Lawrence of Arabia* star
49 Entertains
51 Approximately, datewise
52 Island's surroundings, perhaps
53 Subway of Paris
54 How to play solitaire
55 Nosh
58 Seafood in a shell
59 Shah's country
60 Infamous Roman emperor
61 Right, on a map
63 Fishing gear

★ Ring Links

Find the one set of five linked rings in this picture.

THREE AT A RHYME

Rearrange these letters to form three one-syllable words that rhyme.

A A E E F H O O T U W

_____ _____ _____

★★ Circular Reasoning

Connect all of the circles by drawing a single continuous line through every square of the diagram. All right-angle turns of your line must alternate between boxes containing a circle and boxes not containing a circle. You must make a right-angle turn out of every square that contains a circle. Your line must end in the same square that it begins, and it cannot enter any square more than once.

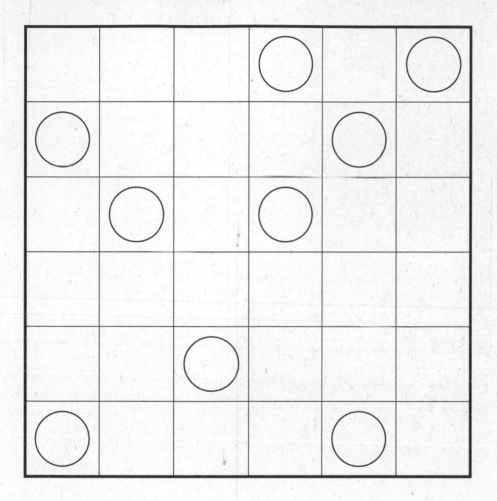

ADDITION SWITCH

Switch the positions of two of the digits in the incorrect sum at right, to get a correct sum.

```
  2 6 6
+ 4 7 5
-------
  6 3 1
```

★ Let's Eat Out

Find the 21 words and phrases associated with restaurants that are hidden in the diagram either across, down, or diagonally. Answers include three two-word phrases and eight plurals ending in S.

```
B  S  I  L  E  R  F  C  G  S  S  P
R  R  B  J  T  R  H  H  R  G  R  U
E  E  S  O  I  D  S  A  A  O  E  H
F  M  T  E  O  I  U  L  T  D  G  C
I  O  S  S  L  T  A  K  U  T  R  T
L  T  S  E  I  F  H  B  I  O  U  E
L  S  R  O  S  G  F  O  T  H  B  K
S  U  F  B  D  E  E  A  Y  K  M  T
D  C  I  A  T  A  N  R  W  Y  A  R
Y  R  E  L  T  U  C  D  H  X  H  I
M  I  L  K  S  H  A  K  E  S  T  B
T  O  L  G  N  I  K  R  A  P  A  W
T  O  P  E  E  F  F  O  C  C  S  C
W  A  I  T  R  E  S  S  Q  I  R  F
B  O  O  T  Z  J  U  K  E  B  O  X
```

TONGUE TWISTER

From what language are all of these words derived:

YOGA, ORANGE, LILAC, and PUNDIT?

A) Sanskrit B) Swahili C) Czech D) Spanish

★ Cornered by Gail Grabowski

ACROSS

1 The "N" in USNA
6 More than impressed
10 Canyon sound
14 Suspect's excuse
15 Fibber
16 Hawaiian feast
17 Neighborhood celebration
19 Newspaper notice
20 Salad-dressing ingredient
21 Lessen
22 Windshield cleaners
24 '50s cool one
26 Fills fully
27 McIntosh, for one
29 Haul a trailer
32 Macaroni shape
35 Skipper's area
36 Self-image
37 Pirate's haul
38 Package-ribbon feature
39 Challenge
40 TV news hour
41 "Shoo!"
43 British noblemen
44 Curved letter
45 Last cars on trains
48 Runway vehicle
50 Supporting actors
54 Boat basin
56 Air-conditioning units: Abbr.
57 Cow comment
58 __ Brockovich
59 Honest transaction
62 Kitchen basin
63 Rotate
64 Washer cycle
65 Droops
66 Top-notch
67 Exams

DOWN

1 Influential person
2 Kate's TV friend
3 Cello cousin
4 2 on a touch-tone
5 Hardly used
6 Nome's state
7 Telegram
8 Gobble up
9 Plaster alternative
10 Get hitched in secret
11 Tenderized beef cut
12 Pigtail material
13 Baseball-scoreboard data
18 Forked over the cash
23 List entry
25 Horse's gait
26 Gush
28 Snapshot
30 Shrek, e.g.
31 Troubles
32 "So what __ is new?"
33 Lane of Superman
34 Bed part
38 Porker of pictures
39 Do a household chore
41 Glance at
42 Card game
43 Menu course
46 Gas-pump rating
47 Tart-tasting
49 Pieces of a chain
51 Prayer endings
52 Bake in an oven
53 Boot bottoms
54 __ around (waste time)
55 La Scala solo
56 Overdo, on the grill
60 Status __
61 Vegas cube

★ Sudoku

Fill in the blank boxes so that every row, column, and 3x3 box contains all of the numbers 1 to 9.

6	3		8		1		5	7
				5				2
		1		7			6	3
			6	8				5
		7		1	9	2	3	4
		9	7		4	1	8	
	7		1	8				
3		6				5		
		4	3	2		6		1

MIXAGRAMS

Each line contains a five-letter word and a four-letter word that have been mixed together (the order of the letters in each word has not been changed). Unmix the two words on each line and write them in the spaces provided. When you're done, find a two-part answer to the clue by reading down the letter columns in the answers.

CLUE: It may come over you

A L L Y O G O W A = _ _ _ _ _ + _ _ _ _

J I D U N T L A Y = _ _ _ _ _ + _ _ _ _

R A P L O D A R P = _ _ _ _ _ + _ _ _ _

K I P W R I S I M = _ _ _ _ _ + _ _ _ _

★ 123

Fill in the diagram so that each rectangular piece has one each of the numbers 1, 2, and 3, under these rules: 1) No two adjacent squares, horizontally or vertically, can have the same number. 2) Each completed row and column of the diagram will have an equal number of 1s, 2s, and 3s.

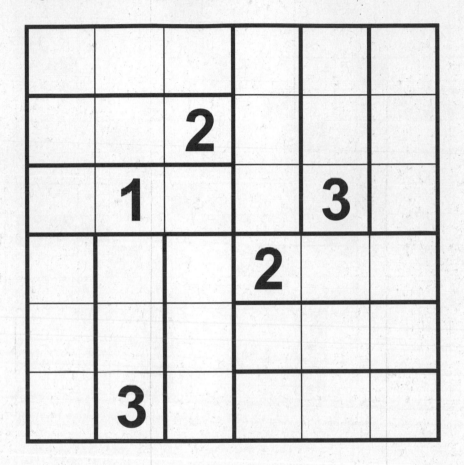

SUDOKU SUM

Without repeating any digits, complete the sum at right, by filling one digit in each of the five blanks.

```
    2 _ 5
  + _ 0 _
  _____
    _ 8 _
```

★ Watch It by Sally R. Stein

ACROSS

1 Kid around
5 Iowa city
9 Hidden supply
14 World's fair, for short
15 Burrowing mammal
16 Comic Hardy's nickname
17 Dalmatian marking
18 Maui or Tahiti
19 Sharp part of a knife
20 Song heard in *Funny Girl*
23 Moose relative
24 Language suffix
25 Pied Piper's followers
26 Seattle clock setting: Abbr.
27 G-man's employer
29 Location
32 Parts of ears
35 Greek-salad ingredient
37 Crow sound
38 Making an appearance
41 __ *for Alibi* (Grafton novel)
42 Coins in France and Spain
43 Young horses
44 Easy throw
46 Tomato color
47 Metallic rock
48 Makes public
50 Fuss
51 Commercials, for example
54 Taking part in a campaign
58 Snapshot
59 Sign on the dotted __
60 Ocean phenomenon
61 Wandered around
62 Keats poems
63 Gymnast Korbut
64 Chicago airport
65 Schoolbook
66 Take a quick look

DOWN

1 Reverend Jackson
2 Kick out
3 *Baby and Child Care* author
4 Dorothy's dog
5 In the center of
6 Dayan of Israel
7 Singer Fitzgerald
8 Observed
9 Snake charmer's snake
10 Parcels out
11 Like Mozart's music
12 Keep a low profile
13 Wide shoe size
21 Legendary Scottish monster, affectionately
22 Be behind the wheel
26 Cathedral bench
27 Inundate
28 Storage containers
30 Diplomacy
31 Rams' mates
32 Exam for an atty.-to-be
33 Where Dayton is
34 Latin American dance
35 Folklore meanie
36 Real-estate bank account
39 Clinic professional
40 Enemy
45 Job for a teen
47 Most peculiar
49 Half of RI
50 Building addition
51 Nimble
52 Evade
53 Move quietly
54 "Yikes!"
55 Ink stain
56 Assistant
57 On the apex of
58 Salaried athlete

★ One-Way Streets

The diagram represents a pattern of streets. A and B are parking spaces, and the black squares are stores. Find the route that starts at A, passes through all stores exactly once, and ends at B. Arrows indicate one-way traffic for that block only. No block or intersection may be entered more than once.

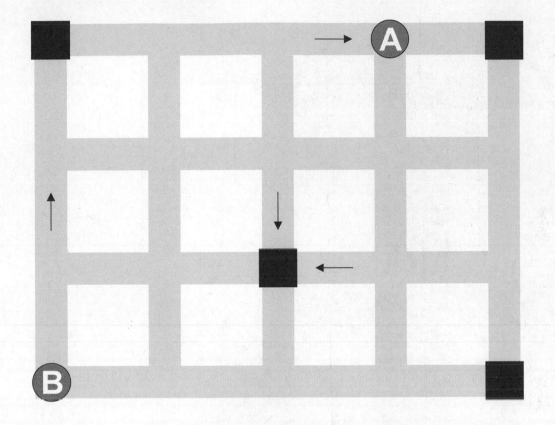

SOUND THINKING

We can think of four common uncapitalized words whose only consonant sounds are B, L, B, and R, in that order. How many can you think of?

_____   _____

_____   _____

★★ Overlap

Three transparent letters, each of a different color, are placed on top of each other in this design. If the three letters were separated, what word would they spell? The color squares below the design are the same as and are in the same order as the three letters in the word.

COMMON SENSE

What three-letter word can be found in the dictionary definitions of all of these words:

COUGAR, FARMER IN THE DELL, LITTER, and SHOO?

— — —

★ Star Search

Find the stars that are hidden in some of the blank squares. The numbered squares indicate how many stars are hidden in the squares adjacent to them (including diagonally). There is never more than one star in any square.

TELEPHONE TRIOS

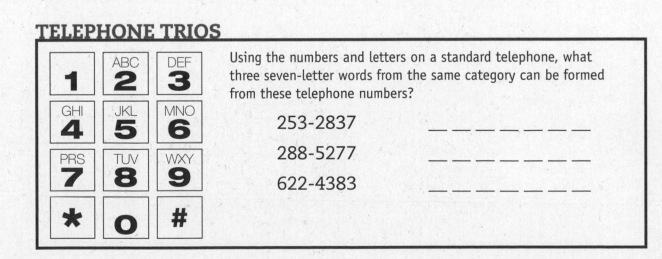

Using the numbers and letters on a standard telephone, what three seven-letter words from the same category can be formed from these telephone numbers?

253-2837 _ _ _ _ _ _ _

288-5277 _ _ _ _ _ _ _

622-4383 _ _ _ _ _ _ _

★ On the Surface by Gail Grabowski

ACROSS

1 West Point student
6 Hourglass filler
10 Part of R&R
14 Fragrance
15 Busy as __
16 Barber's expertise
17 Hamburger, essentially
19 __ Stanley Gardner
20 Long period of time
21 On an even __ (steady)
22 Tot's toy
24 Cardigan or crew neck
26 Compass direction
27 Most overbearing
29 Faucet
32 Arrive at a total
35 Defense org. since 1949
36 Spanish cheer
37 Horse's pace
38 Heelless shoes
40 Winter precipitation
41 Make a blunder
42 Cabbage salad
43 Track events
44 Prepare, as a table
45 Joke teller
48 Routine task
50 Pillage
54 South Pacific island
56 Gracious
57 "The Raven" author
58 Skater's leap
59 Geologist's specimen
62 Actual
63 Like a skyscraper
64 Dutch flower
65 Poisonous snakes
66 Retired planes: Abbr.
67 Perfect places

DOWN

1 Homes for parakeets
2 Cupid's projectile
3 Lorna __
4 Australian bird
5 Summer garment
6 Cavalry weapons
7 Brother of Cain
8 Maiden-name indicator
9 Thaws
10 Fictional Butler
11 Neutral color
12 Window ledge
13 Ash or elm
18 Low grades
23 Coupe or convertible
25 Be next to
26 Bicycle part
28 Filled with wonder
30 Tons (of)
31 Church benches
32 Years and years
33 Take a chance
34 Very inexpensive
38 Bouquet creators
39 Flimsy, as an excuse
40 Members of Congress: Abbr.
42 Edinburgh native
43 Authoritative order
46 Shop tools
47 Fleming and McKellen
49 Ant mounds
51 The Big __ (New York City)
52 Former general Powell
53 Holds onto
54 Scarlett's home
55 Woodcutters' tools
56 Tartan garment
60 Western treaty grp.
61 Stick-in-the-__

★ On Safari

Find the 18 words and phrases associated with a safari that are hidden in the diagram either across, down, or diagonally. One of the answers is SAFARI; the rest are for you to find. Answers include one two-word phrase and seven plurals ending in S.

```
E E L E P H A N T S S T
V L X F P S E I X B Y S
R A K P N O R U I R E U
E N C E E A L N D F K D
S D K T F D O E F P N U
E R E A K C I A T J O L
R O S M U E R T E N M I
V V H L A I N E I G A O
W E A Q G G P Y Y O V N
A R S L A M I N A M N S
S J U N G L E S K R A P
S D R E H A N Q M A L G
```

IN OTHER WORDS

There is only one common uncapitalized word that contains the consecutive letters KIO. What's the word?

_____

bRaiN BREaTHER
BETTER COOKING WITH BEER

Many of us would agree that a frosty mug of beer is a delicious addition to any meal, but who knew that *cooking* with it can also yield scrumptious results? Here are amazing culinary uses for our favorite brews:

For a delicious corn side dish, simmer corn kernels in beer for 2 minutes, then drain and stir in butter and seasonings.

For a new spin on lemonade, use beer instead of water. Mix together beer, lemon-lime soda, fresh lemon or lime juice, and sugar.

To make a quick marinade for pork tenderloin, mix together dark beer, molasses, herbs, onion, garlic, and freshly ground black pepper.

To soften up tough, inexpensive cuts of beef, pour a can of beer over the meat, and let it soak in for about an hour before cooking it. Even better, marinate the beef overnight in the fridge or put the beer in your slow cooker with the meat.

To deepen the flavor of stews and chilis, stir in 6 ounces beer as you add broth to your favorite recipes.

To doctor up store-bought barbecue sauce, stir in ¼ cup dark beer per cup of sauce.

To give battered and fried fish a shot of flavor, mix together 1½ cups all-purpose flour, ½ teaspoon salt, ¼ teaspoon cayenne pepper, and 1 bottle stout or dark beer.

For Belgian-style steamed mussels, simmer the mussels in a covered pot with beer (lager or ale is best; avoid dark beers), clam broth, chopped tomatoes, garlic, onions, and fresh basil or parsley.

For tastier corned beef and cabbage, add half a bottle of brown beer to the pot while the corned beef and cabbage are simmering.

To give grilled chicken a Southwestern twist, mix together 6 ounces beer and 1 can (15 ounces) red enchilada sauce. Add 1½ pounds boneless, skinless chicken breasts or thighs, and marinate in the refrigerator 4 to 8 hours. Grill or broil the chicken (this chicken is delicious when sliced and served on warm tortillas with salsa, vegetables, and sour cream).

★★ Line Drawing

Draw three straight lines, each from one edge of the square to another edge, so that the letters in each of the six regions spell a word of a different length.

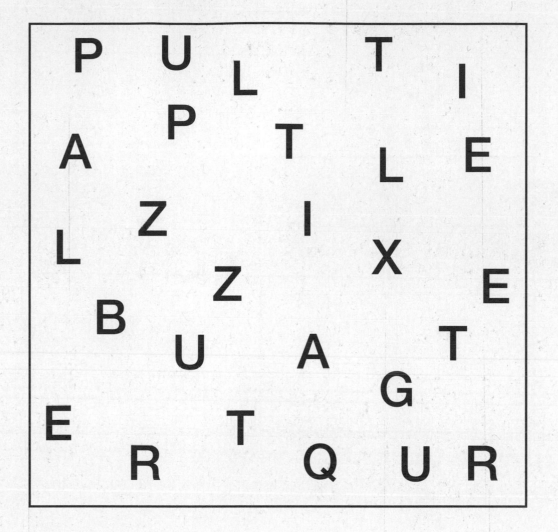

THREE OF A KIND

Find the three hidden words in the sentence that, read in order, go together in some way.

The ballet school had to relinquish a key dancer
to stage *Delilah and Samson*.

★ ABC

Enter the letters A, B, and C into the diagram so that each row and column has exactly one A, one B, and one C. The letters outside the diagram indicate the first letter encountered, moving in the direction of the arrow. Keep in mind that after all the letters have been filled in, there will be one blank box in each row and column.

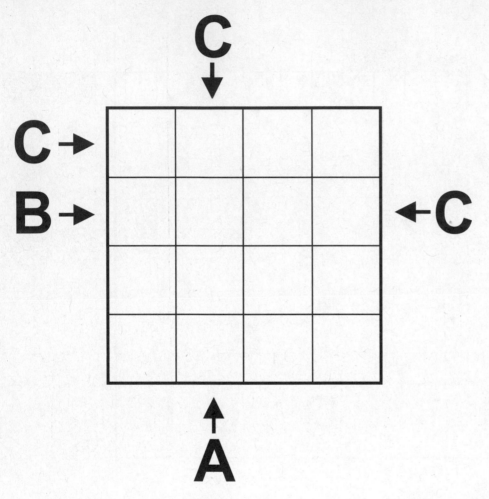

CITY SEARCH

Use the letters in MELBOURNE to form common uncapitalized six-letter words. We found five of them. How many can you find?

_ _ _ _ _ _   _ _ _ _ _ _   _ _ _ _ _ _

_ _ _ _ _ _   _ _ _ _ _ _

★ In a Spin by Sally R. Stein

ACROSS

1 Facing the pitcher
6 __ gin fizz
10 1 Down's title: Abbr.
14 Jockey's mount
15 Cougar
16 Best-selling cookie
17 Playing marble
18 Bullfight cheers
19 Baseball officials
20 Capital of Louisiana
22 Aroma detector
23 Talk a lot
24 Where Vienna is
26 Legacy recipient
30 __ boom bah
32 Lemon meringue, for one
33 Otherwise
34 Tennis star Sampras
36 Earlier
40 Cattle farm
42 Lawn material
43 Grocery or boutique
44 Produce blossoms
45 Escorted trip
47 Was obligated to
48 Steal from
50 601, to Caesar
51 Avoid an F
52 Phone operator's device
56 Behave
58 Leave the stage
59 Superfluous part
65 Moore of *A Few Good Men*
66 Butter substitute
67 Surpass
68 Metric weight
69 Back area
70 '70s vice president
71 Diminutive suffix
72 Makes a mistake
73 Intends

DOWN

1 *Moby-Dick* character
2 Roman's robe
3 Mischievous child
4 Concerning
5 Very small
6 Most eerie
7 Doozy
8 Last Greek letter
9 Relent
10 Kitchen surface
11 Knight's suit
12 Coca-Cola competitor
13 Where sailors go

21 Hoarse sound
25 Soup samples
26 Cooking additive
27 Airline of Israel
28 "Ignorance of the law __ excuse"
29 Sports-almanac stat
31 Got to one's feet
35 Principals and professors
37 Nebraska neighbor
38 Sources of silver
39 Lipstick shades

41 Medical-insurance cos.
46 Highly caloric
49 Earlier
52 Botanical fence
53 Use, as influence
54 Draw a bead on
55 Ceramic installer
57 Wee hour
60 Feeling of dread
61 Immense
62 Volcano of Sicily
63 Biblical garden spot
64 Weather systems

★★ Tri-Color Maze

Find the shortest route through the maze, entering at the top and exiting at the bottom. You must pass over the color sections in this sequence: red, blue, yellow, red, blue, etc. Change colors by passing through a white square. It is okay to retrace your path.

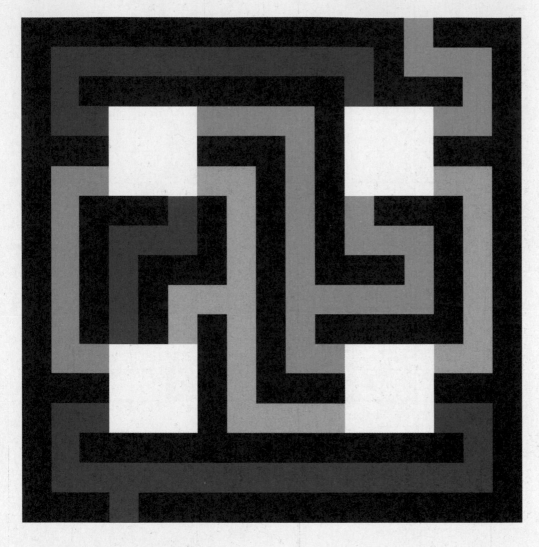

BETWEENER

What four-letter word belongs between the word at left and the word at right, so that the first and second word, and the second and third word, each form a common two-word phrase?

WAITING __ __ __ __ PRICE

★ Puzzle Wiz

Find these words associated with the 1939 film *The Wizard of Oz* that are hidden in the diagram either across, down, or diagonally. As indicated by the two slash marks in the word list, NO PLACE and LIKE HOME are hidden separately, as are YELLOW and BRICK ROAD.

```
K M M S H U R R I C A N E N E Z
F D U M R J U D Y G A R L A N D
C O S U P E L J B E R T L A H R
T R I N R Y P F A O D A N R O T
I O C C O R W P R C N N W A R B
W T A H F N I E I A K A I I F A
D H L K E E C L M L N H M A A E
E Y W I S H K A M E S K A N R H
K G R N S E E G C Q E Y B L I B
C A D S O L D Y Y O O I B A E T
I L N Z R C W H C V U L T U U Y
W P E S M N I T L W S R L N R M
R K C T A U T O O G I G A E U B
E X A M R S C R N Y L S M G Y A
Q F L U V Z H O O I C E S E E Z
H C P S E J S D N A R A N W O D
C N O I L Y L D R A W O C F A H
L U N C I H A E L T L O O O I S
U T R A E H C D I C U D R C Y C
G O T A T R C N Y R R K K E F I
S T R O O I M C A A C O K A A G
S J T W T A H G Z I R N R U R A
I T G Y C O L I R Y O F A E M M
M Y E L L O W B E M O H E K I L
```

AUNTIE EM
BERT LAHR
BRAIN
COURAGE
COWARDLY LION
CYCLONE
DOROTHY GALE
EMERALD CITY
FARM
GLINDA
HEART
HICKORY
HURRICANE
JACK HALEY
JUDY GARLAND
KANSAS
L FRANK BAUM
MAGIC
MISS GULCH

MONKEYS
MUNCHKINS
MUSICAL
NO PLACE / LIKE
  HOME
PROFESSOR MARVEL
RUBY SLIPPERS
SCARECROW
SONGS
TIN MAN
TORNADO
TOTO
UNCLE HENRY
WICKED WITCH
WISH
WIZARD OF OZ
YELLOW / BRICK
  ROAD
ZEKE

INITIAL REACTION

The "equation" below contains the initials of words that will make it correct, forming a numerical fact. Solve the equation by supplying the missing words.

$$435 = \text{M. of C. in the H. of R.}$$

_____

★ Find the Ships

Determine the position of the 10 ships listed to the right of the diagram. The ships may be oriented either horizontally or vertically. A square with wavy lines indicates water and will not contain a ship. The numbers at the edge of the diagram indicate how many squares in that row or column contain parts of ships. When all 10 ships are correctly placed in the diagram, no two of them will touch each other, not even diagonally.

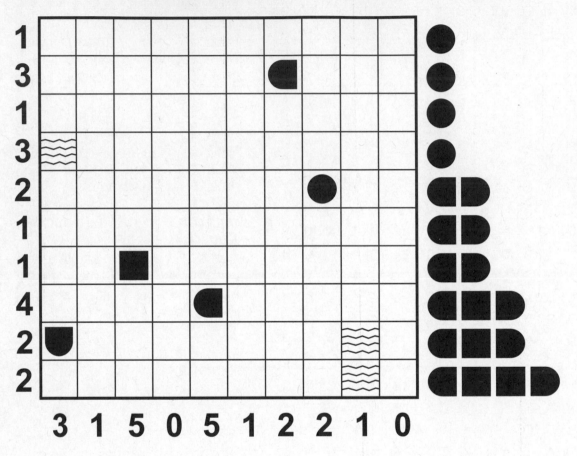

TWO-BY-FOUR

The eight letters in the word PROFOUND can be rearranged to form a pair of common four-letter words in four different ways. Can you find all four pairs of words?

_ _ _ _   _ _ _ _

_ _ _ _   _ _ _ _

★★ Sudoku

Fill in the blank boxes so that every row, column, and 3x3 box contains all of the numbers 1 to 9.

1			3		9	4		8
3		5			1	2	9	
			2			6	3	
5	8	4	1		6	3		
6				5	3			
	3			2	4			9
2	5	6		1				
		9	6	3	7			
8			5					

MIXAGRAMS

Each line contains a five-letter word and a four-letter word that have been mixed together (the order of the letters in each word has not been changed). Unmix the two words on each line and write them in the spaces provided. When you're done, find a two-part answer to the clue by reading down the letter columns in the answers.

CLUE: Paris has one

C U L A B U G E H = _ _ _ _ _ + _ _ _ _

T E X U R D E A M = _ _ _ _ _ + _ _ _ _

F A N C U N S E T = _ _ _ _ _ + _ _ _ _

T I N K U B Y E R = _ _ _ _ _ + _ _ _ _

★ Below the Belt by Gail Grabowski

ACROSS

1 Girl's garment
6 Glasgow residents
11 Boxer's punch
14 Spooky
15 Sports complex
16 GI show sponsor
17 Skimpy summer garments
19 Bashful
20 Young goat
21 Defrost
22 Fills completely
24 Pittsburgh footballer
26 Shave, as a sheep
28 Capri-style garments
32 Control the car
35 Have lunch
36 Pasture
37 Traditional knowledge
38 P.O. box item
39 Rather and Marino
40 Boxer Muhammad
41 "I kid __ not"
42 __ sense (ESP)
43 Some trousers
48 Country singer Patsy
49 Sunbather's goal, perhaps
53 Weight monitor
55 Dust particle
56 Go quickly
57 Heavy weight
58 Flared-leg garments
62 Historical period
63 Nimble
64 Insertion mark
65 Actor Gibson
66 Cow catchers
67 Red-deer females

DOWN

1 Classroom items
2 Come to bat again
3 Wear away
4 Knight's title
5 Pioneer
6 African desert
7 Black bird
8 Above, in poems
9 Explosive initials
10 Talks back to
11 "Hey, calm down!"
12 Tennis champ Arthur
13 Young men
18 Storage building
23 Ooh and __
25 Fencing blade
26 Practice in the ring
27 Makeshift shelter
29 Slow down, as rainfall
30 Tenant's expense
31 Window part
32 Smack
33 Turnpike fee
34 Waterway opened in 1825
38 Miner's strike
39 Floppy __
41 Longing
42 Lengthen, as a rubber band
44 __ in the Family
45 Man's jewelry clasp
46 Pueblo homes
47 Global alliance
50 Rosebush sticker
51 Pointed (at)
52 Robins' homes
53 Peony part
54 Apple center
55 French miss: Abbr.
59 Self-image
60 Facial feature
61 Mai __

★ Circular Reasoning

Connect all of the circles by drawing a single continuous line through every square of the diagram. All right-angle turns of your line must alternate between boxes containing a circle and boxes not containing a circle. You must make a right-angle turn out of every square that contains a circle. Your line must end in the same square that it begins, and it cannot enter any square more than once.

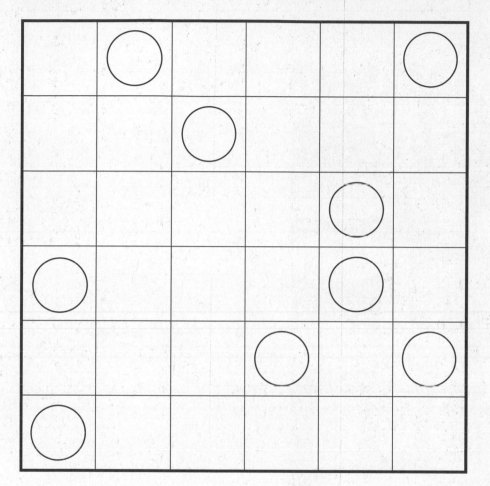

ADDITION SWITCH

Switch the positions of two of the digits in the incorrect sum at right, to get a correct sum.

$$\begin{array}{r} 502 \\ +994 \\ \hline 803 \end{array}$$

★★ Triad Split Decisions

In this clueless crossword puzzle, each answer consists of two words whose spellings are the same, except for the consecutive letters given. All answers are common words; no phrases or hyphenated or capitalized words are used. Some of the clues may have more than one solution, but there is only one word pair that will correctly link up with all the other word pairs.

TRANSDELETION

Delete one letter from the word INDICATIVE and rearrange the rest, to get a type of health-care professional.

_____

★ 123

Fill in the diagram so that each rectangular piece has one each of the numbers 1, 2, and 3, under these rules: 1) No two adjacent squares, horizontally or vertically, can have the same number. 2) Each completed row and column of the diagram will have an equal number of 1s, 2s, and 3s.

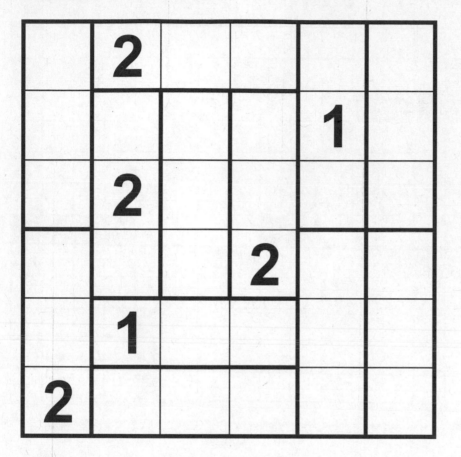

SUDOKU SUM

Without repeating any digits, complete the sum at right, by filling one digit in each of the four blanks.

```
  4 _ 3
+ _ 6 _
-------
  5 _ 2
```

★ Betting Setting by Gail Grabowski

ACROSS

1 *Daily Planet* reporter Lane
5 Flat-topped hills
10 Owl sound
14 Wyatt of the Old West
15 Share one's views
16 Strongly encourage
17 Largest continent
18 Trace of color
19 Colt's mother
20 Radio-station employee
22 Malt beverages
23 Clip, as wool
24 Picnic spoiler
26 Breakfast or brunch
29 Baby beds
33 Poison-ivy reaction
37 Make a sketch
39 Roof overhangs
40 Immigration island
42 '50s White House nickname
43 Hardly enough
44 Mexican friend
45 Bumper bump
47 Finishes
48 Nature trails
49 "That's enough!"
51 Off the __ (out of trouble)
54 Outstanding obligations
58 Farm storage building
61 Audio portion of a movie
65 Skunk's defense
66 Suez or Panama
67 Shah's land, once
68 Diana of the Supremes
69 Full of pep

70 "That's __ than enough!"
71 Otherwise
72 Movie critic, often
73 Beef dish

DOWN

1 Show the way
2 Desert rest area
3 From Dublin
4 Elbow room
5 Went for a drive
6 Heroic tale
7 Descend
8 Infuriate
9 "So long!"
10 Mankind
11 Unwritten exam
12 Folklore meanie
13 Golf platforms
21 Traffic snarl
25 Chills, as a drink
27 Dry as a bone
28 Huron and Michigan
30 Lendl of tennis
31 Road curve
32 Retired planes: Abbr.
33 Harvest
34 __ mater
35 Narrow cut
36 Haughty attitude
38 Departed
41 Fair to middling
46 Two-year-old
50 Beagle or bunny
52 Hollywood award
53 Australian animal
55 Hat edges
56 Fortune-teller's deck
57 Frighten
58 Feeling angry
59 Pop star, perhaps
60 Election defeat
62 Military group
63 Central area of a church
64 Was aware of

★ Islands

Shade in some of the white squares in the diagram with "water," so that each remaining white box is part of an island. Each island will contain exactly one numbered square, indicating how many squares that island contains. Each island is separated from the other islands by water but may touch other islands diagonally. All water is connected, but there are no 2x2 regions of water in the diagram.

3		2		
			3	
3				

AND SO ON

Unscramble the letters in the phrase FARE LINK, to form two words that are part of a common phrase that has the word AND between them.

_____ and _____

★★ The Green Stuff

Find the eight green things that are hidden in the honeycomb. Form your words by moving from one letter tile to another as long as they share a side in common. All tiles must be used exactly once.

COMMON SENSE

What three-letter word can be found in the dictionary definitions of all of these words:

BUSYBODY, CROWBAR, INTERFERE, and POKE?

— — —

★ Green Party

Find the fifteen green things that are hidden in the diagram either across, down, or diagonally.

```
Q S Y E L S R A P
H U H F Y U B L C
S C R A E G M E L
U U A N M A S T O
T L V N R R S T V
C Y I T I A O U E
A A I M E P J C R
C A K P E S S E K
N E M E R A L D Z
B R O C C O L I N
E G A B B A C R M
```

TONGUE TWISTER

From what language are all of these words derived:

COCKATOO, SARONG, ORANGUTAN, and BAMBOO?

A) Dutch B) Persian C) Portuguese D) Malay

★ Beastly Bunches by Shirley Soloway

ACROSS

1 Letter between phi and psi
4 School grps.
8 Canvas cover
12 Fictional Finn
14 Jeans maker Strauss
15 Salad veggie
17 Exile isle
18 Iowa city
19 AM/FM device
20 Clan self-respect
23 Linguistic suffix
24 Jimmy of *The West Wing*
25 Shoe parts
27 Not in school
30 Got up
31 Computer shortcut
32 Climbing plant
34 Weaponry
37 German "I"
38 Green Bay footballers
41 Batman and Robin, e.g.
42 Opportunity, slangily
44 Comic Carey
45 Some harness races
47 Desert spots
49 Taken care of
50 Pacific Ocean discoverer
52 Extended an invitation to
54 Pirate's quaff
55 Form a crowd
60 Adjust to a situation
62 Keep __ (persist)
63 Fencing blade
64 Sad song
65 Lose energy
66 A few
67 Bradley or Sharif
68 Slugger's stat
69 Agree silently

DOWN

1 Food Network figure
2 Luau dance
3 Military weapon: Abbr.
4 __ *Again, Sam*
5 Entice
6 States as fact
7 Strong Spanish assent
8 Matador
9 Santa __, CA
10 Supervise closely
11 Self-assurance
13 German emperor of old
16 Votes against
21 Pre-Q queue
22 One with nerve
26 Civil War side: Abbr.
27 French friends
28 __, Beethoven and Brahms
29 Frontier teacher
30 From the top
32 TV attachments
33 Adlai's opponent
35 Mongrel
36 Not very good
39 *Let's Make __* (game-show oldie)
40 Take the helm
43 Bar bill
46 Makes over
48 Less harsh
49 Takes to the ice
50 Thin nail
51 Video partner
52 Intermission follower
53 "Mini" or "maxi" clothing
56 Witness' affirmation
57 Second word in a fairy tale
58 *Nautilus* captain
59 Proof of ownership
61 Tiger Woods' org.

★★ One-Way Streets

The diagram represents a pattern of streets. A and B are parking spaces, and the black squares are stores. Find a route that starts at A, passes through all stores exactly once, and ends at B. Arrows indicate one-way traffic for that block only. No block or intersection may be entered more than once.

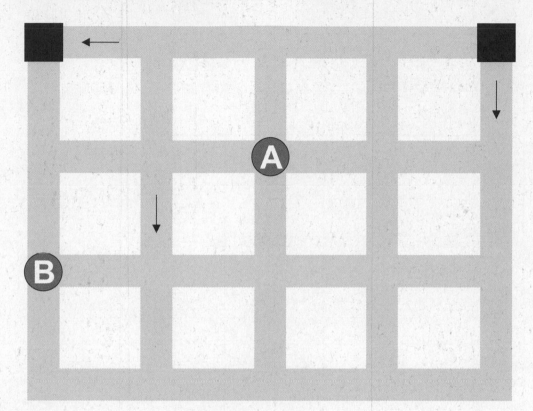

SOUND THINKING

We can think of four common uncapitalized words whose only consonant sounds are T, R, T, and R, in that order. How many can you think of?

_____   _____

_____   _____

★ Hyper-Sudoku

Fill in the blank boxes so that every row, column, 3x3 box, *and* each of the four
3x3 gray regions contains all of the numbers 1 to 9.

	4	5			9		8	2
					6	3		4
		9	4		2		1	
		1		2		8		9
					1		3	5
	3				5		2	
5	1	4			8	9	6	
		6	5	9		4		1
	7							

COUNTDOWN

Inserting plus signs and minus signs, as many as necessary, in between the digits from 9 to 1
below, create a series of additions and subtractions whose final answer is 45. Any digits without
a sign between them are to be grouped together as a single number.

9   8   7   6   5   4   3   2   1   =   45

★ Star Search

Find the stars that are hidden in some of the blank squares. The numbered squares indicate how many stars are hidden in the squares adjacent to them (including diagonally). There is never more than one star in any square.

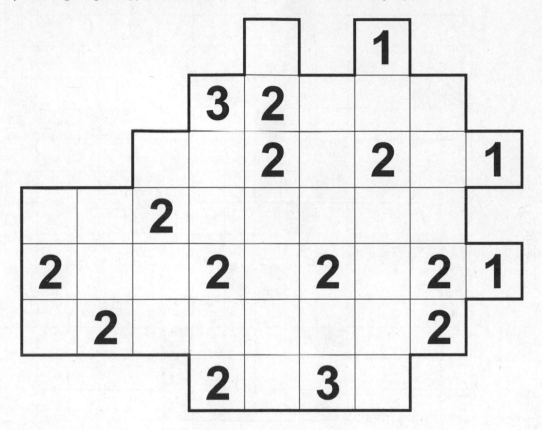

TELEPHONE TRIOS

1	ABC 2	DEF 3
GHI 4	JKL 5	MNO 6
PRS 7	TUV 8	WXY 9
*	0	#

Using the numbers and letters on a standard telephone, what three seven-letter words from the same category can be formed from these telephone numbers?

242-7747   _ _ _ _ _ _ _

782-7837   _ _ _ _ _ _ _

228-8379   _ _ _ _ _ _ _

★ School Subjects by Gail Grabowski

ACROSS

1 Hollywood award
6 Scorch
10 Window section
14 Concise
15 Seldom seen
16 Scored 100 on
17 Golf hazards
18 Curved lines
19 Guys-only party
20 Not at work
21 Social worker's record
24 Travels with the band
26 Reaches across
27 Friendly ghost of comics
29 Ceremony
31 Arthur of tennis
32 Forget to include
34 Louisiana cuisine
39 King of beasts
40 More sensible
42 Mystical message
43 Run out, as a subscription
45 Jules Verne captain
46 Division word
47 Singer Loretta
49 It's north of California
51 Artist Picasso
54 One of the senses
55 Player's motion to assist the ball
58 CPR pro
61 Table extension
62 Darling
63 Bicker
65 Jane Austen novel
66 One of the Great Lakes
67 In __ (fashionable)
68 Cold War rival: Abbr.
69 Cincinnati baseballers
70 Macho males

DOWN

1 Director Preminger
2 Medieval worker
3 Hobbyists' hangout
4 Poisonous snake
5 Save from harm
6 Rude
7 Long-eared hopper
8 Foot feature
9 Don't go quietly
10 Penne or ziti
11 Follow, as advice
12 Gets closer to
13 Anxious
22 Cupid's missile
23 On __ (without a contract)
25 Unlocks
27 Ring up
28 China's continent
29 Ascended
30 Agenda detail
33 Wisc. neighbor
35 Disney mermaid
36 Playground apparatus
37 "Do __ others ..."
38 Sign gas
41 Hotel offerings
44 *Vogue* rival
48 Over there
50 Go over again
51 "The Raven" and "Annabel Lee"
52 Washington's successor
53 To a great degree
54 Fathers
55 __ cheese dressing
56 Richard of *Chicago*
57 __-back (easygoing)
59 Stubborn animal
60 New driver, often
64 Numbered hwy.

★ ABC

Enter the letters A, B, and C into the diagram so that each row and column has exactly one A, one B, and one C. The letters outside the diagram indicate the first letter encountered, moving in the direction of the arrow. Keep in mind that after all the letters have been filled in, there will be one blank box in each row and column.

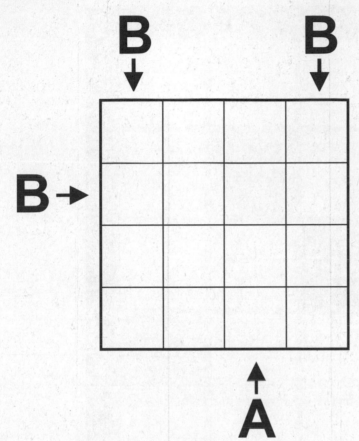

CLUELESS CROSSWORD

Complete the crossword with common uncapitalized seven-letter words, based entirely on the letters already filled in for you.

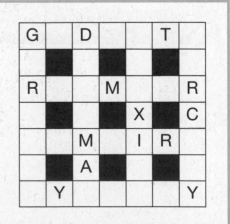

★★ Looped Path

Draw a continuous, unbroken loop that passes through each of the red, blue, and white squares exactly once. Move from square to square in a straight line or by turning left or right, but never diagonally. You must alternate passing through red and blue squares, with any number of white squares in between.

BETWEENER

What four-letter word belongs between the word at left and the word at right, so that the first and second word, and the second and third word, each form a common two-word phrase?

MOTOR __ __ __ __ RUN

★★ Sudoku

Fill in the blank boxes so that every row, column, and 3x3 box contains all of the numbers 1 to 9.

		6		3	5			8
5				7				
8	7		2	9			6	1
	4			1	6		2	7
			8			3	4	
	2	8	7					
			6				8	5
6		9						
2								4

MIXAGRAMS

Each line contains a five-letter word and a four-letter word that have been mixed together (the order of the letters in each word has not been changed). Unmix the two words on each line and write them in the spaces provided. When you're done, find a two-part answer to the clue by reading down the letter columns in the answers.

CLUE: Actor's difficulty?

A T H R E I R C S = _ _ _ _ _ + _ _ _ _

P A M T O I S O S = _ _ _ _ _ + _ _ _ _

F A R L A G U Y E = _ _ _ _ _ + _ _ _ _

M O D E D R E L Y = _ _ _ _ _ + _ _ _ _

★ I Love a 49 Down by Sally R. Stein

ACROSS

1 Headquartered
6 Prepares for a boxing match
11 TV room device
14 Prefix for violet
15 23 Across procedure
16 Anger
17 Scientist Pasteur
18 Prepare Parmesan, perhaps
19 Young beagle
20 Second-string athlete
22 Electrified fish
23 Tax agcy.
24 Before the deadline
26 Ship's kitchen
30 Eagle claw
33 Israeli leader Sharon
34 Computer pointing devices
35 Elaborate party
39 Maximum auto acceleration, so to speak
42 Back talk
43 Sewing-needle feature
44 Share and share __
45 Chopin piece
47 Dinnerware dishes
48 Black playing card
51 Actor Mineo
52 __-tac-toe
53 Southeast vacation spot
61 College cheer
62 Bowling alleys
63 Showed a show again
64 Numero __
65 Kitchen appliances
66 Singer Reese
67 Cow sound
68 Not at all nice
69 Visit Dreamland

DOWN

1 Tulip-to-be
2 Lotion ingredient
3 Flabbergast
4 Norse explorer __ the Red
5 Author Hammett
6 Epic stories
7 Contented cat sound
8 Abel's father
9 Religious ceremony
10 Sound system
11 Poisonous snake
12 Not at all nice
13 Answer
21 Distorted, as a grin

25 Actress Lansbury
26 Disparities
27 General vicinity
28 Jar covers
29 Took, as an apartment
30 Info on a book spine
31 Feel sore
32 Iacocca or Trevino
34 Frame of mind
36 Going __ (fighting)
37 Huron or Michigan
38 Pub servings
40 Day before Fri.
41 Certain ducks
46 Skillet coating

47 Tablet
48 Play the guitar
49 Theme of the puzzle
50 Sound of a sneeze
51 Mama's boy
54 Molten rock
55 Small bills
56 Take, as an apartment
57 On an even __ (balanced)
58 Author __ Stanley Gardner
59 New Haven university
60 Zipper alternative

★★ Line Drawing

Draw two straight lines, each from one edge of the square to another edge, so that the letters in each of the four regions spell a different mood.

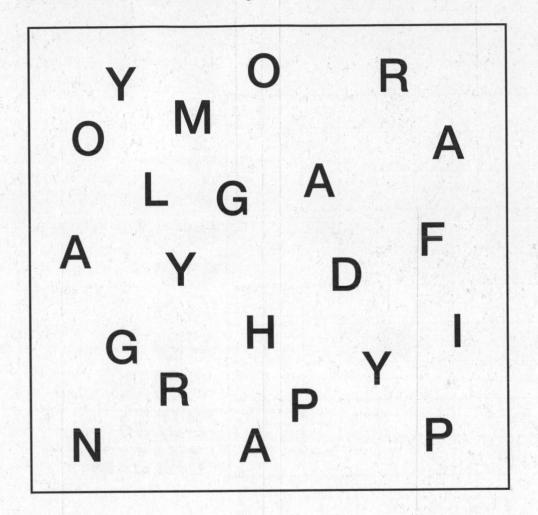

THREE OF A KIND

Find the three hidden words in the sentence that, read in order, go together in some way.

The regatta began in the harbor; rowing in haste, Alabama beat Oberlin.

★ Find the Ships

Determine the position of the 10 ships listed to the right of the diagram. The ships may be oriented either horizontally or vertically. A square with wavy lines indicates water and will not contain a ship. The numbers at the edge of the diagram indicate how many squares in that row or column contain parts of ships. When all 10 ships are correctly placed in the diagram, no two of them will touch each other, not even diagonally.

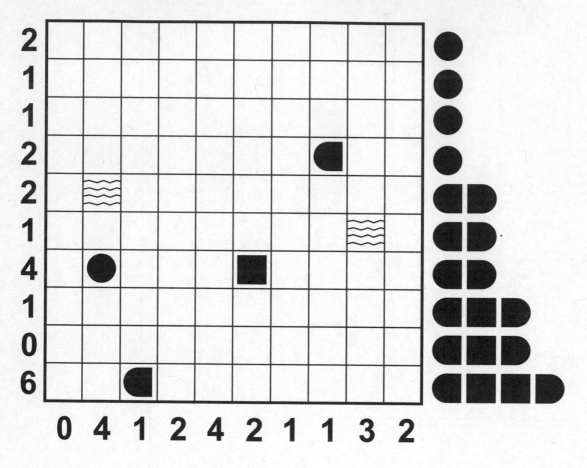

TWO-BY-FOUR

The eight letters in the word ULTIMATE can be rearranged to form a pair of common four-letter words in two different ways, if no four-letter word is repeated. Can you find both pairs of words?

_ _ _ _　_ _ _ _

_ _ _ _　_ _ _ _

★★ Circular Reasoning

Connect all of the circles by drawing a single continuous line through every square of the diagram. All right-angle turns of your line must alternate between boxes containing a circle and boxes not containing a circle. You must make a right-angle turn out of every square that contains a circle. Your line must end in the same square that it begins, and it cannot enter any square more than once.

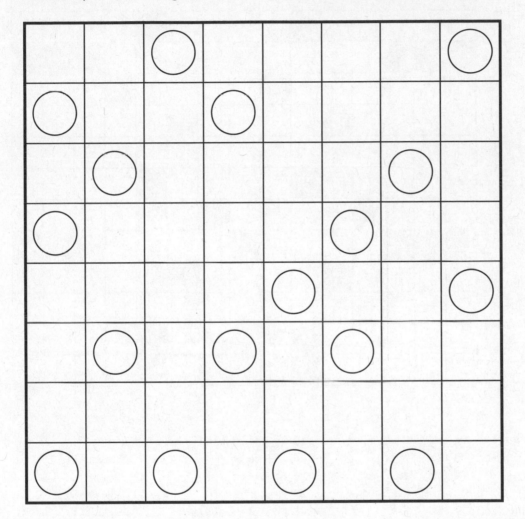

ADDITION SWITCH

Switch the positions of two of the digits in the incorrect sum at right, to get a correct sum.

$$\begin{array}{r} 685 \\ +110 \\ \hline 861 \end{array}$$

★ Valentine's Day Gifts by Sally R. Stein

ACROSS

1 Tulsa's state: Abbr.
5 Not quite hot
9 Portrait holder
14 Curriculum section
15 Director Kazan
16 Artist's stand
17 Valentine's Day gifts
20 Produce, as a play
21 Throat-clearing sound
22 Stalactite site
23 Things to pucker
25 __ 1 (speed of sound)
27 Cash-register key
30 Vanished
31 Skirt border
34 Business letter abbr.
35 British prep school
37 Worker bee
39 Valentine's Day gifts
42 __ of Troy
43 Defeat in boxing
44 "Beware the __ of March"
45 Metallic rock
46 Huntley or Atkins
48 Stubborn
50 Ball-__ hammer
51 Gorillas, for instance
52 Jai __
55 Sound of a crowd
57 In any way
61 Valentine's Day gifts
64 Employee's extra pay
65 Simplify
66 Actress Moreno
67 Poker rituals
68 Gush
69 Ship pole

DOWN

1 Yours and mine
2 Necktie feature
3 Capital of Peru
4 Immediately, just by looking
5 Drenched
6 Assumed name
7 Well-to-do
8 Was profitable
9 Swampy ground
10 Cattle farm
11 On a cruise, perhaps
12 TV producer Griffin
13 Alternatively
18 Astronaut Armstrong
19 "__ Old Cowhand"
24 Fruit covering
26 Hand over legally
27 Mexican snack
28 None of the above
29 Fur coat
30 Reached
31 Unruly crowd
32 Go in
33 Not at all neat
36 Write things down in class
38 Cloudburst
40 Fairy-tale starter
41 Earring shape
47 "Present!"
49 Back part
50 Make angry
51 Stood up
52 Diplomat Eban
53 Lake bird
54 Mom's sister
56 PDQ
58 Pakistan's locale
59 "Shall we?" response
60 Atty.-to-be's exam
62 Battleship letters
63 Hardly any

★★ Bead Maze

Enter the maze at left, pass through all the beads exactly once, then exit. You may not pass through two beads of the same color in a row.

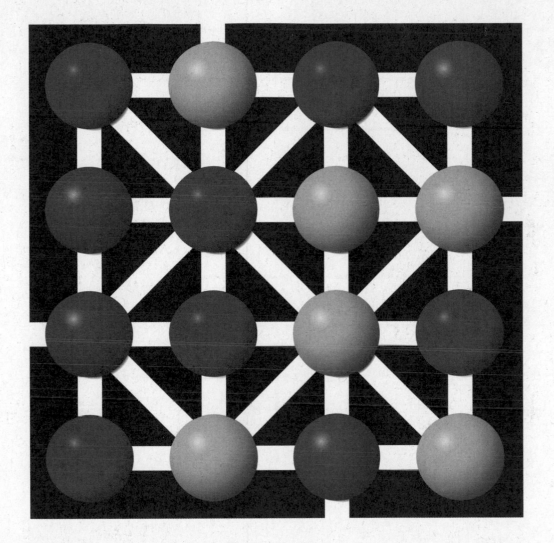

THREE AT A RHYME

Rearrange these letters to form three one-syllable words that rhyme.

C C E E E I J M O O P R S S U U

_____   _____   _____

★★ 123

Fill in the diagram so that each rectangular piece has one each of the numbers 1, 2, and 3, under these rules: 1) No two adjacent squares, horizontally or vertically, can have the same number. 2) Each completed row and column of the diagram will have an equal number of 1s, 2s, and 3s.

	3							
1					1			
		3						3
						3		
			1					
				3				
							2	
		2		2				

SUDOKU SUM

Without repeating any digits, complete the sum at right, by filling one digit in each of the five blanks.

$$\begin{array}{r} \_\ 3\ 9 \\ +\ 7\ \_\ \_ \\ \hline \_\ \_\ 5 \end{array}$$

★ Islands

Shade in some of the white squares in the diagram with "water," so that each remaining white box is part of an island. Each island will contain exactly one numbered square, indicating how many squares that island contains. Each island is separated from the other islands by water but may touch other islands diagonally. All water is connected, but there are no 2x2 regions of water in the diagram.

1				
	2		4	

AND SO ON

Unscramble the letters in the phrase REAL WORD, to form two words that are part of a common phrase that has the word AND between them.

_____ and _____

★ Anatomy 101 by Gail Grabowski

ACROSS

1 Rodeo rope
6 On the peak of
10 Hourglass filler
14 Invite to enter
15 Naughty deed
16 Really impressed
17 "Rise and __!"
18 AMA members
19 Corn Belt state
20 Coffee-break time
21 Burglar's device
24 Sets loose
26 Go inside
27 Law enforcement group
29 Bottle stopper
31 Ireland, in poetry
32 Salon job
34 Treaties
39 Eyeglass part
40 Water vapor
42 Flippant
43 Lugged
45 Scarlett's home
46 `"Guilty" or "not guilty"
47 Agenda unit
49 Cabin cruiser's kitchen
51 Wedding path
54 Part of the upper arm
55 Bodybuilder's seaside hangout
58 Garden tool
61 Just sitting around
62 Belonging to us
63 Off-white color
65 Property claim
66 Move like a butterfly
67 San Francisco footballer, briefly
68 Be defeated
69 Head for the hills
70 V-formation fliers

DOWN

1 The __ of the Mohicans
2 Tennis champ Arthur
3 Penny pincher
4 Do wrong
5 "Just a moment!"
6 South American mountains
7 Saw or sander
8 Without repetition
9 Teen's wall hanging
10 Holy one
11 Heard the alarm
12 More recent
13 June 6, 1944
22 Hangs on to
23 Peeling potatoes, to a GI
25 Remove the soapsuds
27 Animal skin
28 Sandwich cookie
29 Dairy product
30 Actor Sharif
33 Suffix with kitchen
35 Pie fruit
36 Beeper alternative
37 Plum or palm
38 Stick around
41 Illusionist's act
44 Pickle flavoring
48 Start, in golf
50 Feeling sore
51 Sound portion
52 South Pacific spots
53 Part of a play
54 Moisten the turkey
55 Steelmaking factory
56 Male cow
57 Buffalo's lake
59 Raw metals
60 Brontë governess
64 Compete (for)

★★ Go with the Flow

Enter the maze at bottom right, pass through all the stars, then exit. You must go with the flow, making no sharp turns, and may use paths more than once.

COMMON SENSE

What three-letter word can be found in the dictionary definitions of all of these words:

CONQUER, FAVORITE, LANDSLIDE, and WORLD SERIES?

— — —

★★ Split Decisions

In this clueless crossword puzzle, each answer consists of two words whose spellings are the same, except for the consecutive letters given. All answers are common words; no phrases or hyphenated or capitalized words are used. Some of the clues may have more than one solution, but there is only one word pair that will correctly link up with all the other word pairs.

TRANSDELETION

Delete one letter from the word CAMERAS and rearrange the rest, to get a type of sound.

_____

★ Hyper-Sudoku

Fill in the blank boxes so that every row, column, 3x3 box, *and* each of the four 3x3 gray regions contains all of the numbers 1 to 9.

9		1		6	7			4
		2				5		
3	4	8				6		
			9	8	4	1		7
7							5	
		2		5	3			9
	9		8	4				
4	3		5		9			6
	2					9	4	

MIXAGRAMS

Each line contains a five-letter word and a four-letter word that have been mixed together (the order of the letters in each word has not been changed). Unmix the two words on each line and write them in the spaces provided. When you're done, find a two-part answer to the clue by reading down the letter columns in the answers.

CLUE: A little salt water

S W I P A L T E D = _ _ _ _ _ + _ _ _ _

V I P U R D E R O = _ _ _ _ _ + _ _ _ _

C H A B E R A L O = _ _ _ _ _ + _ _ _ _

S P U D R E N E P = _ _ _ _ _ + _ _ _ _

★ Load It Up by Gail Grabowski

ACROSS

1 Snowman's eye material
5 Santa's toy holders
10 Stuntman Knievel
14 School corridor
15 Whooping bird
16 Evaluate
17 Laos locale
18 Filmmaker Woody
19 Diarist Frank
20 Complicated procedures
22 Coupe or convertible
23 Entangle
24 Turn loose
27 Thaw
30 Military greeting
33 Scottish girl
37 *Gone With the Wind* plantation
39 Pertaining to ships
40 Thing on a list
41 Baby's neckwear
42 Sandwich shop
43 Rounded roofs
45 Psychic reader
47 __ Stanley Gardner
48 Said "cheese"
50 Dance move
52 Group of ships
54 Examinations
58 __ Baba
60 Messenger schedule listing
64 Unaccompanied
66 Tuckered out
67 Internet auction site
68 Unwritten exam
69 Don't throw away
70 Barbed __
71 Relate
72 Lock of hair
73 Matinee days: Abbr.

DOWN

1 Burn slightly
2 Desert rest area
3 Adjust, as wheels
4 Camel's South American kin
5 Bright red
6 Folk singer Guthrie
7 Use the phone
8 Prepare to propose
9 Hearing and sight
10 Important time
11 British Columbia city
12 Sicilian peak
13 Impolite look
21 Sleeve filler
25 Light brown
26 Forest clearing
28 Experiment sites
29 Attempts
31 Lofty
32 Author Wiesel
33 Jar tops
34 Molecule part
35 Tournament round
36 Scent
38 Support in crime
44 Take notice of
46 Fixes a piano again
49 Leave the premises
51 Get-up-and-go
53 Floor installer
55 One-pot dinners
56 Leg bone
57 Like a straight A student
58 Considerably
59 Traditional knowledge
61 Hint
62 Smooch
63 Facial features
65 Kay follower

★ Three-for-One Word Search

Find the five hidden words in each of the three diagrams, either across, down, or diagonally. A hint to each group of words is found above each diagram.

SIGNS

```
A Y C S R P K
R O G R I V S
B N E S M E Z
I W C L I J O
L E D R P F H
S B A E T I H
X U L V A G Q
```

SHADES

```
Y O S D X N I
P R R Z E V D
M A W E I R Q
A N R O C G H
J G L B L U E
L E A K O V U
T R F B T E N
```

WORKSHOP

```
L D R I L L C
R E M M A H F
P J S M B S U
E L S I N V Y
K R A Z H T W
P D W N L C I
H Q G X E O A
```

IN OTHER WORDS

There is only one common uncapitalized word that contains the consecutive letters DTE. What's the word?

_____

bRain BREatHer
SURPRISING FACTS ABOUT AMERICA

We all know who the first president was, and the tales behind our country's most important dates and milestones. Here are a few surprising facts about our nation that even the biggest history buffs probably don't know:

America's capital—and by "capital," we mean, where Congress met—has been located in *nine* different cities. Philadelphia, Pennsylvania, has been the most frequent capital (it was the country seat on four different occasions). Lancaster, Pennsylvania, was the shortest-lived U.S. capital—its tenure lasted for just one day in 1777. Washington, D.C., has been the capital since 1800.

* * *

There was once a state named after founding father Benjamin Franklin! Franklin petitioned for recognition as the 14th state, and Thomas Jefferson backed the plan. But Franklin needed the support of nine of the original 13 states, and only seven states approved. Franklin later became part of the Tennessee Territory; that state was admitted to the Union in 1796.

* * *

America didn't have time zones or a standardized time until 1883. Until that year, time was told by sunrise and sunset because most citizens worked the land. With the rise of the railroad industry in the 19th century, though, minutes really began to matter. Congress passed the Standard Time Act, which legalized Standard Railway Time, in 1918.

* * *

New York became the first state to adopt electrical execution. The shocking law went into effect on January 1, 1889.

* * *

The first Christmas tree to grace New York's Rockefeller Center went up in 1931—yes, during the Great Depression. It was decorated with tin cans, paper, and tinsel. Unlike today's more vertical versions, the tree was only 12 feet tall.

* * *

The circus first came to America in 1793. John Bill Ricketts and his troupe dazzled their Philadelphia audience, George Washington among them (one of Washington's horses, Jack, was actually incorporated into the show). Ricketts' amphitheaters in Philadelphia and New York unfortunately burned to the ground six years later, which brought bankruptcy to our nation's first circus show.

★★ One-Way Streets

The diagram represents a pattern of streets. P's are parking spaces, and the black squares are stores. Find the route that starts at a parking space, passes through all stores exactly once, and ends at the other parking space. Arrows indicate one-way traffic for that block only. No block or intersection may be entered more than once.

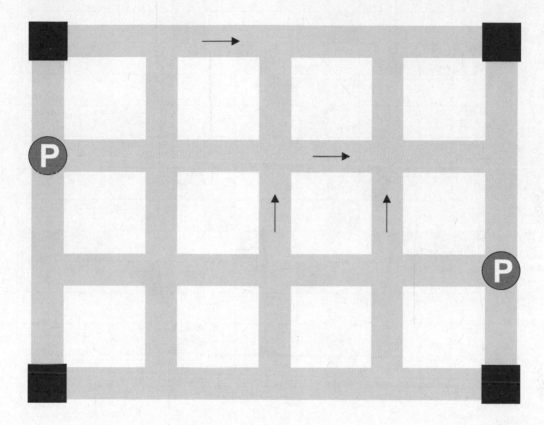

SOUND THINKING

The consonant sounds in the term HOI POLLOI are H, P, and L. We can think of two common uncapitalized single words whose only consonant sounds are also H, P, and L, in that order. How many can you think of?

_____   _____

★ Georges by Sally R. Stein

ACROSS

1 Molten rock
6 Inept one
10 Reebok rival
14 Fencing swords
15 Man of the hour
16 Great Lake
17 Composer/columnist Georges
20 Weapons
21 Actor Alda
22 Birds' homes
23 Glove filler
25 Mardi __
27 Spin
30 Look at
31 Recipe amts.
35 Author Zola
36 Ross of the Supremes
38 Mon. follower
39 Pollster/author Georges
42 Industrious insect
43 Baseball great Satchel
44 Actress Witherspoon
45 Agenda
47 Form 1040 org.
48 *House of the Seven* __ (Hawthorne novel)
49 In a competent fashion
51 Settles a bill
52 Ease up
55 Service charges
57 Charged atoms
61 Two general Georges
64 Music for three
65 Opera solo
66 Swiss girl of fiction
67 Turn __ (become)
68 2550, to Caesar
69 Sense of humor, for example

DOWN

1 Prefix for bytes or bucks
2 Imitative one
3 Microbe
4 Soldier's cafeteria
5 Campfire residue
6 Youngster
7 Singer Horne
8 Citrus-flavored drink
9 Slip into, as clothing
10 Most recent
11 Part of the eye
12 Scotsman's wear
13 Snakelike swimmers
18 Lose strength
19 Geneticist's molecule
24 Devoured
26 Nevada city
27 Fit for a king
28 Mideast resident
29 Leans to one side
30 Performs in a chorus
32 "Stainless" metal
33 Sign of a heartbeat
34 Tennis star Monica
36 Where cows are milked
37 Impressive grouping
40 Beach-sand holder
41 Internet pages
46 Epidermal art
48 Sound scared
50 Hive dweller
51 Brake or accelerator
52 Start of a play
53 Overcook
54 __ were (so to speak)
56 City in Oklahoma
58 Elevator inventor
59 Junction point
60 Peeved mood
62 Lamb's father
63 Cry of discovery

★★ Sets of Three

Group all the symbols into sets of three, with each set having either all the same shape or all the same color. The symbols in each set must all be connected to each other by a common horizontal or vertical side.

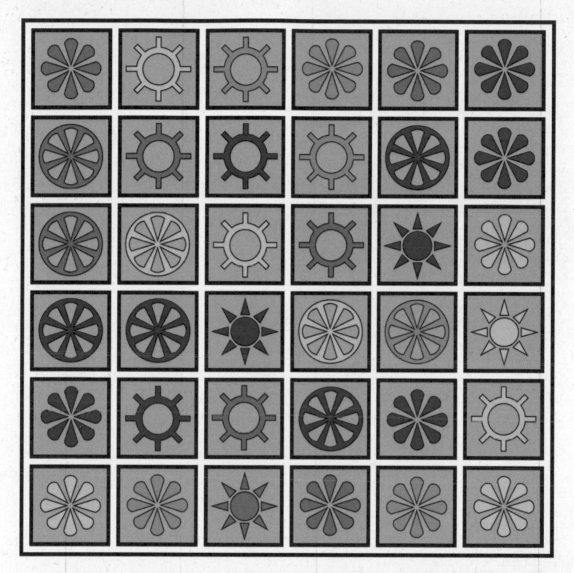

THREE AT A RHYME

Rearrange these letters to form three one-syllable words that rhyme.

A A C H K N O T T T W Y

_____   _____   _____

★★ Star Search

Find the stars that are hidden in some of the blank squares. The numbered squares indicate how many stars are hidden in the squares adjacent to them (including diagonally). There is never more than one star in any square.

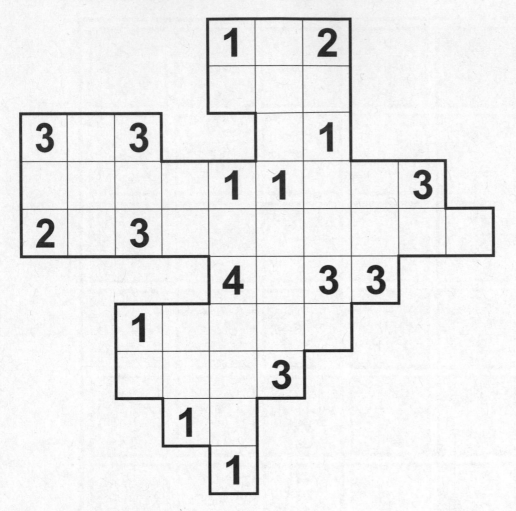

TELEPHONE TRIOS

1	ABC 2	DEF 3
GHI 4	JKL 5	MNO 6
PRS 7	TUV 8	WXY 9
*	O	#

Using the numbers and letters on a standard telephone, what three seven-letter words from the same category can be formed from these telephone numbers?

296-2257   _ _ _ _ _ _ _

742-2656   _ _ _ _ _ _ _

858-5353   _ _ _ _ _ _ _

★★ Triad Split Decisions

In this clueless crossword puzzle, each answer consists of two words whose spellings are the same, except for the consecutive letters given. All answers are common words; no phrases or hyphenated or capitalized words are used. Some of the clues may have more than one solution, but there is only one word pair that will correctly link up with all the other word pairs.

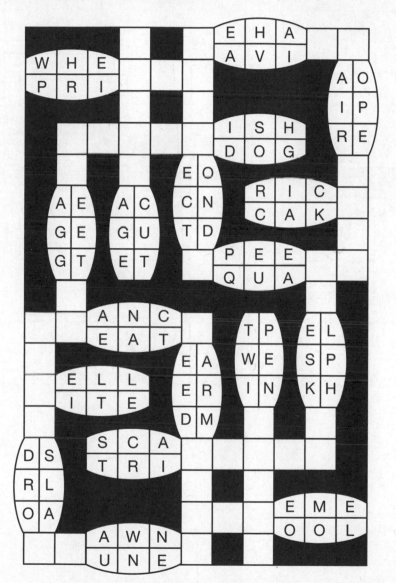

TRANSDELETION

Delete one letter from the word NONPOLITICAL and rearrange the rest, to get a term in botany.

_____

★★ Living Large by Daniel R. Stark

ACROSS

1 Where Tijuana is
5 Pet-shop buy
9 Smiles broadly
14 Grad
15 Astronaut Shepard
16 '80s NBC drama
17 Freeway access
18 "Don't do that!"
19 Comment to the audience
20 Overalls front
21 Hotel reservation request
23 In debt
25 Dwell
26 Sweet-talk
28 Not well done
30 Business partner, perhaps
31 Ready for anything
32 Occurs to, with "on"
33 Baptism, for one
34 Comeback
35 Trucker on the air
39 Jalopies
40 Piano-playing Marx brother
41 Use a paper towel
44 Counting-out word
45 Wine vessel
46 Fortunate
48 Something to fall back on
49 Slopes race
52 Not quite e'er
55 Untrue
56 PDQ
57 Surrealist painter
58 ATM key
59 Water vessel
60 Neighbor of Pakistan
61 Textile workers
62 Actress Lamarr
63 Uptight

DOWN

1 Fishhook part
2 Jai __
3 747, for one
4 Current unit
5 Type of tooth
6 "Moving right __ ..."
7 Criminal group
8 Slaughter of baseball
9 Sports jackets
10 Removes obstacles
11 Exculpatory explanations
12 Managed somehow
13 Nobel's home
21 Clan garb
22 Wry humor
24 Had on
26 Railroad unit
27 __ Baba
28 Daisy Mae's in-law
29 Night fliers
32 Campus figure
34 Offends the nose
35 Honolulu sleuth
36 NYSE, with "the"
37 Environmental prefix
38 Director Howard
39 Torments
40 __ up (be quiet)
41 Endorsed
42 Pungent, perhaps
43 River of Nebraska
45 Computer disk
47 Auto-racing family surname
48 Pattern on a 21 Down
50 Mascara target
51 '70s tennis star
53 Lose energy
54 Wee
57 Tool and __

★★ ABC

Enter the letters A, B, and C into the diagram so that each row and column has exactly one A, one B, and one C. The letters outside the diagram indicate the first letter encountered, moving in the direction of the arrow. Keep in mind that after all the letters have been filled in, there will be two blank boxes in each row and column.

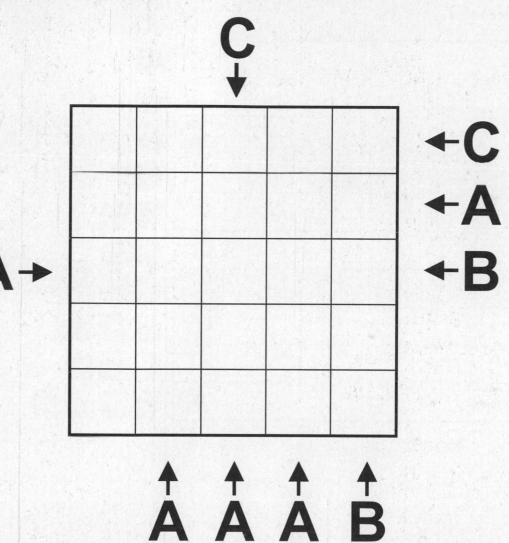

CITY SEARCH

Using the letters in BELGRADE, we were able to form two common uncapitalized seven-letter words. Can you find them both?

— — — — — — —   — — — — — — —

★★ Find the Ships

Determine the position of the 10 ships listed to the right of the diagram. The ships may be oriented either horizontally or vertically. A square with wavy lines indicates water and will not contain a ship. The numbers at the edge of the diagram indicate how many squares in that row or column contain parts of ships. When all 10 ships are correctly placed in the diagram, no two of them will touch each other, not even diagonally.

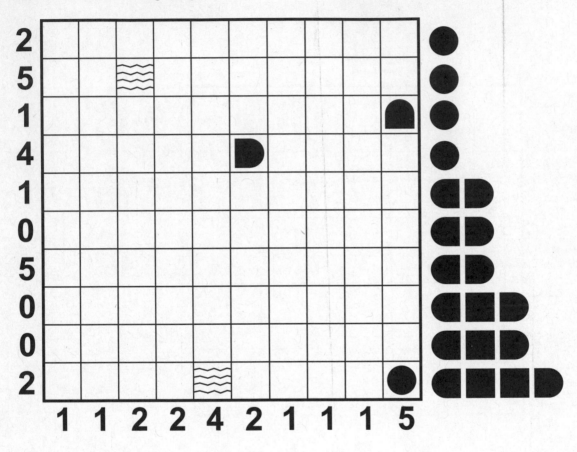

TWO-BY-FOUR

The eight letters in the word CHAMPION can be rearranged to form a pair of common four-letter words in two different ways. Can you find both pairs of words?

_ _ _ _   _ _ _ _

_ _ _ _   _ _ _ _

★★ Wise Guys by Daniel R. Stark

ACROSS

1 "Poison" shrub
6 Overly infatuated
10 Arab League member
14 Loos or Ekberg
15 German song
16 Drink with a burger
17 Forest find
19 2004 Brad Pitt film
20 Writer Tyler
21 Thick heads of hair
22 Use a safety belt
26 Alvarado of *Little Women*
28 Wound up
29 Road without an out
31 Chenille items
32 Joe of *GoodFellas*
33 Musical engagement
35 Luau strings
36 Hotel accommodations
37 Card dealer's box
38 Pay for
39 Alfred and Lynn, to Broadway fans
40 Grass unit
41 Court fine
43 Meshlike fabrics
44 Boot fillers
45 From Rangoon
46 Did nothing
48 Celebratory suffix
49 Corn product
50 Supervise closely
56 Not much
57 Author Hoffer
58 Ear pollution
59 Sluggish
60 Physicist Ernst
61 Morning sweet

DOWN

1 Enervate
2 Mono- relative
3 Hr. fraction
4 Did lunch
5 Party snacks
6 Actor Close
7 Nurse's helper
8 Hair goo
9 Lemony drink
10 Gas-pump info
11 Early forecast
12 __ vera
13 Con votes
18 Oklahoma city
21 Dress style
22 Second-stringer
23 Started studying
24 Meat counter purchase
25 Pub selection
26 Analyzes
27 Speed competition
29 Goddess, for instance
30 Current conduits
32 Fourth-down plays
34 Sixth-day Christmas gift
36 Mope around
37 Urban eyesore
39 Delicate, as fabric
40 Serve suds
42 Celeb opposite
43 Bubble over
45 Gray-barked tree
46 Daily drama
47 Palo __, CA
48 Govt. protector since 1933
50 Sleep phenom.
51 Tax-deferred investment
52 Aussie leaper
53 Ear pollution
54 Columbus sch.
55 Tuna catcher

★★ Shamrock Maze

Start at the center, pass through all the shamrocks, then exit at bottom. You may not retrace your path.

BETWEENER

What five-letter word belongs between the word at left and the word at right, so that the first and second word, and the second and third word, each form a common two-word phrase?

PARKING __ __ __ __ __ STATION

★★ Sudoku

Fill in the blank boxes so that every row, column, and 3x3 box contains all of the numbers 1 to 9.

	1	2			3	7		5
3								4
4		5		7			8	6
2	7		4	5				
5				3			7	
1					9		4	
		1	6			9		3
		3	5				2	
					2			

MIXAGRAMS

Each line contains a five-letter word and a four-letter word that have been mixed together (the order of the letters in each word has not been changed). Unmix the two words on each line and write them in the spaces provided. When you're done, find a two-part answer to the clue by reading down the letter columns in the answers.

CLUE: Big ape

K A S P E O K E K = _ _ _ _ _ + _ _ _ _

S H O W B A M I O = _ _ _ _ _ + _ _ _ _

T E N S E O N E N = _ _ _ _ _ + _ _ _ _

S T U F R O N G G = _ _ _ _ _ + _ _ _ _

★★ Circular Reasoning

Connect all of the circles by drawing a single continuous line through every square of the diagram. All right-angle turns of your line must alternate between boxes containing a circle and boxes not containing a circle. You must make a right-angle turn out of every square that contains a circle. Your line must end in the same square that it begins, and it cannot enter any square more than once.

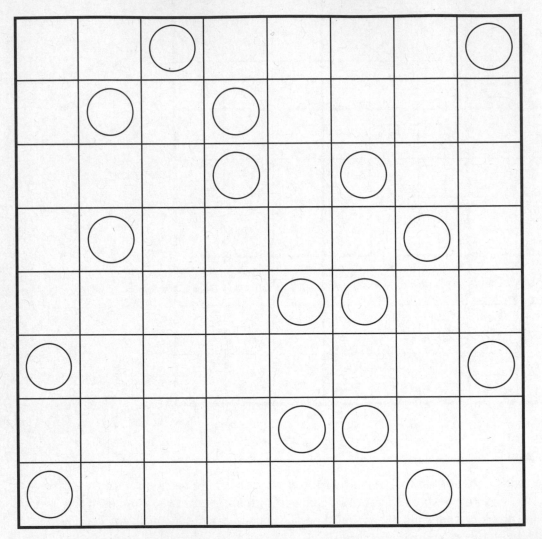

ADDITION SWITCH

Switch the positions of two of the digits in the incorrect sum at right, to get a correct sum.

$$\begin{array}{r} 428 \\ +543 \\ \hline 701 \end{array}$$

★★ Hardware Store by Doug Peterson

ACROSS

1 Globule
5 URL starter
9 Take the mound
14 Leprechaun's land
15 *Field of Dreams* setting
16 Florida citrus center
17 Bona fide
18 Rat-__
19 Amarillo's locale
20 Short, violent rainstorm
23 Excuse starter
24 Powdered grain
25 Frog-throated
27 Playpen dweller
30 Yellow melon
32 Biblical farmer
33 Day division
35 Splinter groups
38 NBC rival
39 Car-engine cooler
41 Keystone lawman
42 *Love Story* author
44 Desert bluff
45 Boss, in Barcelona
46 Slipped away from
48 Pigeon's perch, perhaps
50 Mother of Calcutta
52 Declare openly
53 Raggedy doll
54 Thor weapon
60 Socially smooth
62 Synthesizer inventor
63 Mayberry lad
64 One who takes a shot
65 Starter for legal or military
66 Reputation
67 Gives a holler
68 Does and ewes
69 Oomph

DOWN

1 Oceanic obstacle
2 Stead
3 Kind of vaccine
4 Luggage lugger
5 Longfellow subject
6 Tally up
7 Christmas poem opener
8 Trodden trail
9 Beef entrée
10 1 Down material
11 Accountants' concern
12 Nick name?
13 Alacrity
21 Intense desire
22 Questioning comments
26 Bart's grandfather
27 Hosp. areas
28 Back of the neck
29 Emery-board target
30 To the third power
31 Mars' equivalent
34 "The joke's __!"
36 Soybean product
37 WWI German admiral
39 Causes consternation
40 Seat of Clark County, Nevada
43 Stein filler
45 Samson's weapon
47 Bit of Morse code
49 High crag
50 Scrumptious
51 Accustom (to)
52 Think the world of
55 Strike callers
56 Father of Ham
57 Iridescent gem
58 Soup bean
59 High schooler, usually
61 MPH measure

★★ Islands

Shade in some of the white squares in the diagram with "water," so that each remaining white box is part of an island. Each island will contain exactly one numbered square, indicating how many squares that island contains. Each island is separated from the other islands by water but may touch other islands diagonally. All water is connected, but there are no 2x2 regions of water in the diagram.

		2			
1					
					4
3				2	
3					

AND SO ON

Unscramble the letters in the word ULTRASHOE, to form two words that are part of a common phrase that has the word AND between them.

_____ and _____

★★ Hyper-Sudoku

Fill in the blank boxes so that every row, column, 3x3 box, *and* each of the four 3x3 gray regions contains all of the numbers 1 to 9.

7		8	3				2	5
				7	4			1
4								
					6			
6		9		5	7			
		2	9		5	4		
		1		3	2			
	2	5		8			6	3

COUNTDOWN

Inserting plus signs and minus signs, as many as necessary, in between the digits from 9 to 1 below, create a series of additions and subtractions whose final answer is 3. Any digits without a sign between them are to be grouped together as a single number.

9	8	7	6	5	4	3	2	1	=	3

★★ Ways to Pay by Fred Piscop

ACROSS

1 Bacon partner
5 Lionel Hampton's instrument
10 ITAR-__ (news agency)
14 Ketch or yawl
15 Like a lot
16 Ancient Peruvian
17 Gaucho's weapon
18 Author Ephron
19 School on the Thames
20 Exam grader's option
23 President pro __
24 Pig's digs
25 Baseball manager Joe
28 Hamm of soccer
31 Artichoke center
35 "Gotcha!"
36 Dwarf tree
38 __ culpa
39 Pre-employment routine
42 Psyche part
43 Derby entries
44 Feed the pot
45 Oscar de la __
47 Bard's "always"
48 Intense feeling
49 Santa __ winds
51 Having the blues
52 Light Brigade offensive
59 Sheltered spot
60 River embankment
61 Rowboat needs
63 Aroma
64 Upright
65 Muse of history
66 Rooster-crowing time
67 Class struggles?
68 "Neat!"

DOWN

1 Flow out
2 Icky stuff
3 Big bash
4 Shatner show
5 *Barbarella* director
6 Inventor's start
7 Weevil's meal
8 Norse explorer
9 Roebuck's partner
10 Color, hippie-style
11 One against
12 Dundee native
13 __ Francisco
21 Links peg

22 Set of values
25 Rome's river
26 Missouri feeder
27 Army scout's job
28 Mary Tyler __
29 Occupied
30 He played 28 Down's boss
32 Make changes to
33 Right-hand page
34 Greedy sort
36 Sis' sib
37 PC pop-ups
40 Accra's land
41 Aerosmith's music

46 Place for a brew
48 Motorists' org.
50 Apportion
51 Outbuildings
52 Musical postscript
53 State openly
54 French name
55 French name
56 Minimal change
57 Strong wind
58 New York canal
59 New England catch
62 "That's a joke, __!"

★ Three-for-One Word Search

Find the five hidden words in each of the three diagrams, either across, down, or diagonally. A hint to each group of words is found above each diagram.

NO STANDING

```
W  T  B  L  S  R  D
T  H  R  O  N  E  Q
Y  U  F  O  E  R  Z
P  A  N  T  L  I  V
G  H  T  S  K  A  J
X  E  I  S  E  H  A
S  I  O  M  F  C  C
```

LITTLE PEOPLE

```
Y  P  M  U  R  G  L
H  Y  Y  G  L  U  X
D  A  O  E  F  M  B
O  T  P  H  P  E  D
C  P  S  P  F  O  Z
W  A  N  J  Y  K  D
B  V  A  Q  S  U  H
```

ABOUT TIME

```
D  N  O  C  E  S  A
A  E  N  F  H  R  Q
Y  D  T  O  Y  B  W
T  E  U  U  U  I  C
Z  R  G  J  N  S  H
M  O  N  T  H  I  K
P  L  M  O  V  X  M
```

INITIAL REACTION

The "equation" below contains the initials of words that will make it correct, forming a numerical fact. Solve the equation by supplying the missing words.

9 = I. in a B.G. (if not a T.) _____

★★ Missing Links

Find the one ring in the picture that is not linked to any other.

COMMON SENSE

What four-letter word can be found in the dictionary definitions of all of these words:

CHINESE CHECKERS, LEAPFROG, SPRING, and TRIATHLON?

— — — —

★★ Holdups by Fred Piscop

ACROSS

1 Something to scratch
5 Redford, in *The Natural*
10 Fork over
13 Light carriage
14 Put to rest
15 Sheltered spot
16 Garment holder-upper
18 Lena of *Chocolat*
19 Never revealed
20 Going stag
22 __ out a living
23 Bumped into
25 Casino game
26 *The Kiss* sculptor
28 Organ grinder's aide
32 Western elevation
35 Bit of gossip
37 Booby trap
38 Word form meaning "height"
39 Backs of necks
41 Hill dwellers
42 Italics feature
44 Zippo
45 Consider
46 Vascular starter
48 French textile city
50 "Slippery" trees
52 __ standstill
53 Pointer
56 Ogden Nash's priest
60 Type of skiing
62 Arp's art
63 Stagecoach holder-upper
65 __ 500
66 Skylit courts
67 Give temporarily
68 Dissenting vote
69 Not reputable
70 Former spouses

DOWN

1 Magazine edition
2 Ideated, nonstandardly
3 Social stratum
4 Shot in the arm, for short
5 Submitted, as homework
6 Timeworn
7 Wasn't colorfast
8 Ehud of Israel
9 Gambler's strategy
10 Vaulter's need
11 Hertz rival
12 Cravings

15 Architectural holder-upper
17 *Blondie* boy
21 Eve's grandson
24 Giant of myth
26 Ballgame holder-upper
27 Tibet neighbor
29 Orson Welles role
30 Art Deco master
31 Assent to a schoolmarm
32 Fem.'s opposite
33 Singer Fitzgerald
34 Magi guide

36 Radio, TV etc.
40 Save for the future
43 Cash drawer
47 Plains Indians
49 Tra __
51 Common surname
53 Seiko alternative
54 Cockamamie
55 Is unresolved
56 Thor's father
57 Granny
58 Whirling water
59 Taj Mahal site
61 Sitcom Marine
64 Stowed away

★★ One-Way Streets

The diagram represents a pattern of streets. P's are parking spaces, and the black squares are stores. Find the route that starts at a parking space, passes through all stores exactly once, and ends at the other parking space. Arrows indicate one-way traffic for that block only. No block or intersection may be entered more than once.

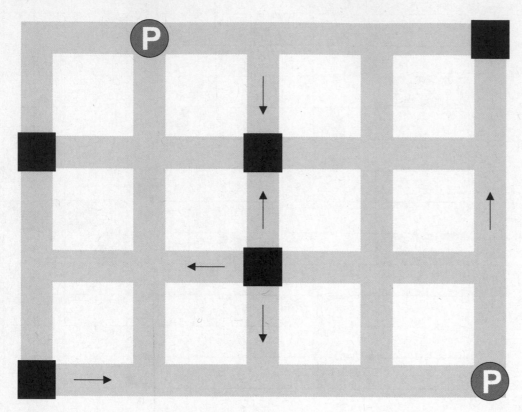

SOUND THINKING

We can think of only one common uncapitalized word whose only consonant sounds are V, K, and D, in that order. What's the word?

_____

★★ 123

Fill in the diagram so that each rectangular piece has one each of the numbers 1, 2, and 3, under these rules: 1) No two adjacent squares, horizontally or vertically, can have the same number. 2) Each completed row and column of the diagram will have an equal number of 1s, 2s, and 3s.

SUDOKU SUM

Without repeating any digits, complete the sum at right, by filling one digit in each of the five blanks.

$$\begin{array}{r} 2\ 4\ \_ \\ +\ \_\ \_\ 9 \\ \hline \_\ \_\ 6 \end{array}$$

★★★ Line Drawing

Draw three straight lines, each from one edge of the square to another edge, so that the letters in each of the five regions spell a different country.

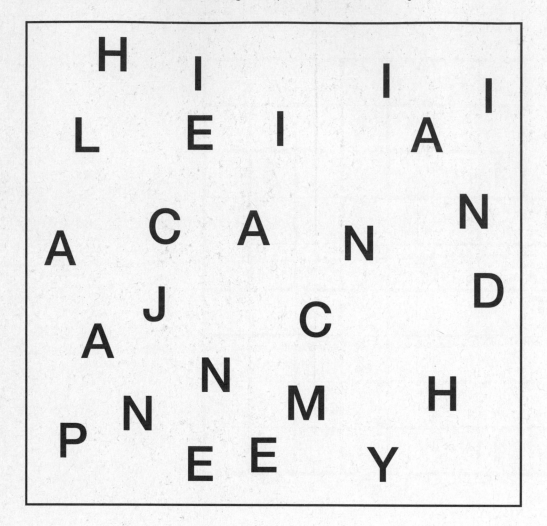

THREE OF A KIND

Find the three hidden words in the sentence that, read in order, go together in some way.

As a psychic dreamer, I can predict events across the next dimension.

★★ Completely by Fred Piscop

ACROSS

1 Red veggie
5 Snake sound
9 Hay bundles
14 Subtle glow
15 Supply-and-demand subj.
16 Fictional Heep
17 Showy bloom
18 Hawaiian port
19 Young girl
20 Prohibit entrance
23 __ Aviv
24 That woman
25 Grind __ halt
26 Guileful
27 Sesame confection
31 Little devils
33 Burger topper
34 Shed tears
36 Llama land
40 Do a grocer's chore
43 Ike Turner ex
44 Sword handle
45 "Mule Train" singer
46 Author Harte
48 Like a duke
49 Indy sponsor
52 Keats creation
53 La __, Bolivia
54 Guffaw syllable
55 Zip down the road
61 Mentally quick
63 Sedan or coupe
64 Place for a roast
65 Bookstore aisle
66 New driver, often
67 Blood fluids
68 Shelled out
69 Lith. and Ukr., once
70 Easy pace

DOWN

1 Bondsman's concern
2 Austrian coin
3 Clapton of rock
4 Thing to do
5 Snicker sound
6 Not so cordial
7 Auction cry
8 Most snobbish
9 Unjust charge
10 *Exodus* role
11 Santa's mail
12 Studio stand
13 In a demure manner
21 Show gratitude to
22 Get-up-and-go
27 Parasite's home
28 Opposed to
29 Sphinx, in part
30 Glossary material: Abbr.
32 Pie-in-the-face sound
34 Lab experiment subjects
35 Sushi fish
37 Good's antithesis
38 Actress Russo
39 Pre-owned
41 Vamp Bara
42 *My Fair Lady* lady
47 Elder Alda
48 Condor's clutchers
49 Former rulers of Iran
50 Try to score, perhaps
51 Beef grade
53 Flying Pan
56 Feels regret over
57 Got beaten
58 Eggs order
59 Roman emperor
60 Pesky swarmer
62 Actor Chaney

★★ Star Search

Find the stars that are hidden in some of the blank squares. The numbered squares indicate how many stars are hidden in the squares adjacent to them (including diagonally). There is never more than one star in any square.

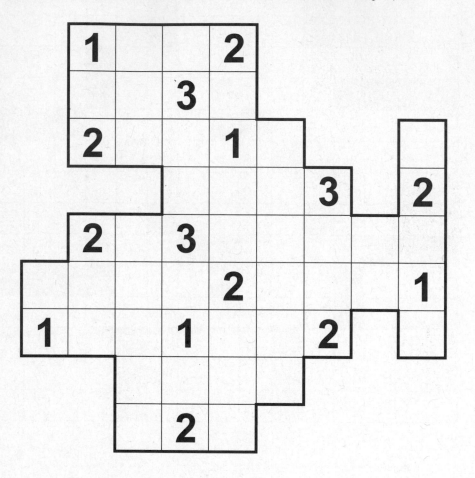

TELEPHONE TRIOS

1	ABC 2	DEF 3
GHI 4	JKL 5	MNO 6
PRS 7	TUV 8	WXY 9
*	O	#

Using the numbers and letters on a standard telephone, what three seven-letter words from the same category can be formed from these telephone numbers?

482-5426   _ _ _ _ _ _ _

772-6474   _ _ _ _ _ _ _

625-8373   _ _ _ _ _ _ _

★★ Straight Ahead

Enter the grid at one of the white squares at left, pass through all the blue squares, then leave the grid through another white square. You must travel horizontally or vertically in a straight line, and turn only to avoid passing through a black square.

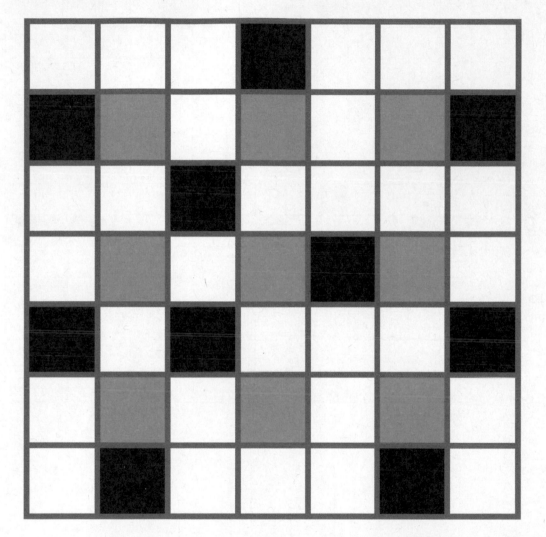

THREE AT A RHYME

Rearrange these letters to form three one-syllable words that rhyme.

A B D D D E H I O R R R W

_____   _____   _____

★★ Straighten Up by Doug Peterson

ACROSS

1 Hen home
5 Menlo Park middle name
9 Distinctive doctrines
13 October birthstone
14 Vietnam neighbor
15 Ice-cream order
16 Physics lead-in
17 Pinball foul
18 Rude dude
19 Draftsman's aid
22 Prefix for angle
23 Gehrig or Mantle
24 Project Apollo mission
26 Jay's competitor
28 Football coach Ewbank
29 Free-for-all
33 Arthur __ Stadium
35 Unskilled laborer
38 Movie-industry concern
40 City near Disney World
42 Army grub
43 TV's Warrior Princess
45 Born first
46 Right on a map
48 Reason to study
50 Debatable point
53 Haile Selassie followers
58 Have brunch
59 Peter Pan adversary
61 Backbone
63 Public houses
64 Raison d'__
65 Gets winded
66 Refer to
67 Behind schedule
68 Novelist Ferber
69 Onion covering
70 Prairielike

DOWN

1 Snug
2 Wagner work
3 Like some cereals
4 Broad board
5 Tennis great Gibson
6 Not of the cloth
7 Encyclopedia books
8 The Jetsons' pet
9 German pronoun
10 Indiana city
11 Havana's __ Castle
12 Leave, slangily
15 Script section
20 Hands over
21 One taking an oath
25 Flower part
27 Flower holder
29 *The Wizard of Oz* studio
30 Poetic preposition
31 Board game penalty
32 English class assignment
34 It's not for real
36 Lyrical tribute
37 Neither partner
39 Bonus
41 Willy the salesman
44 Felix Unger, for one
47 Big bags
49 Up and about
50 *Beau* __
51 Speedy
52 Momentous tales
54 Place for knickknacks
55 Tally up
56 Major vessel
57 Shooting sport
60 Opposed to
62 Teachers' org.

★★ Hyper-Sudoku

Fill in the blank boxes so that every row, column, 3x3 box, *and* each of the four 3x3 gray regions contains all of the numbers 1 to 9.

					4			
	2				9			
8	1	7				3	4	
	9	8		3		7		
4				5		9		
	3			4				
				8		2		
		2		6			9	
7					2	1	5	

MIXAGRAMS

Each line contains a five-letter word and a four-letter word that have been mixed together (the order of the letters in each word has not been changed). Unmix the two words on each line and write them in the spaces provided. When you're done, find a two-part answer to the clue by reading down the letter columns in the answers.

CLUE: Dealer's need

J	U	F	L	I	D	O	E	R	=	_ _ _ _ _	+	_ _ _ _
P	U	L	N	E	L	A	I	T	=	_ _ _ _ _	+	_ _ _ _
P	U	L	C	O	T	E	U	S	=	_ _ _ _ _	+	_ _ _ _
L	I	C	A	M	B	O	K	E	=	_ _ _ _ _	+	_ _ _ _

★★ ABC

Enter the letters A, B, and C into the diagram so that each row and column has exactly one A, one B, and one C. The letters outside the diagram indicate the first letter encountered, moving in the direction of the arrow. Keep in mind that after all the letters have been filled in, there will be two blank boxes in each row and column.

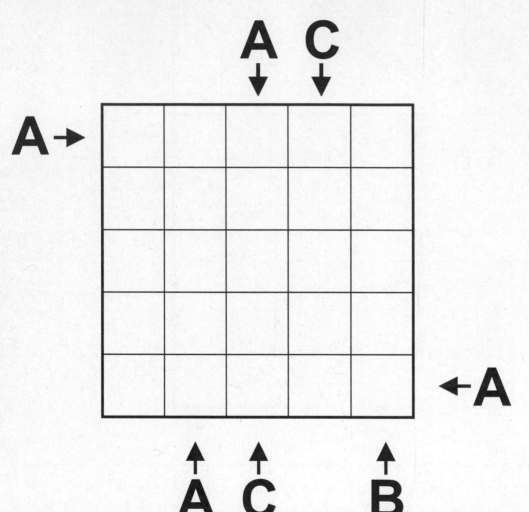

CITY SEARCH

Use the letters in MONTEVIDEO to form common uncapitalized eight-letter words. We found three of them. How many can you find?

_ _ _ _ _ _ _ _   _ _ _ _ _ _ _ _

_ _ _ _ _ _ _ _

★★ Baker's Quartet by Fred Piscop

ACROSS

1 Shut forcefully
5 Casual drive
9 Toss into the trash
14 Fast-food drink
15 Cartoon possum
16 Pageant crown
17 Golden-__ (senior)
18 Auth. unknown
19 Lawn neatener
20 Chuck Berry's genre
23 Battery size
24 Yalie
25 Witch trials town
27 Most spiteful
32 Northern Italian
35 Keats composition
36 Warns
38 "In that case ..."
39 Paper buys
41 Aussie hopper
42 Ali's jabs
43 Jessica of *Dark Angel*
44 Body art
46 Ill temper
47 Bob or beehive
49 Operatic voices
51 Musk, e.g.
53 Suffix for differ
54 Anti-fraud agcy.
56 July 4 noisemaker
62 Letter carrier's beat
64 Singer Fitzgerald
65 Not fooled by
66 Burger topper
67 Not much
68 Fax a page, say
69 Allotted, with "out"
70 Capture on video
71 Afternoon socials

DOWN

1 Lasting impression
2 Company symbol
3 Actor Guinness
4 Trading center
5 Sporting dog
6 Water-lily locale
7 Inventor Sikorsky
8 They're taboo
9 "__ by Starlight"
10 El __ (Spanish hero)
11 Street urchin
12 Neighborhood
13 Law assistant, for short
21 "Wanted" poster name
22 Track circuits
26 Singer Adams
27 Grammy winner Jones
28 __ Rogers St. Johns
29 Horse hero of a 2003 film
30 Medical fluids
31 Runs easily
33 Houston pro
34 Fronts of airplanes
37 Dorothy Gale's dog
40 __ Antony
42 Fictional Doone
44 Singer Braxton
45 Do business
48 Stand up for
50 Without profit
52 Take the tab
54 Gift label word
55 Muscular fitness
57 Exile isle
58 Film fragment
59 Patch place
60 Sicilian spewer
61 Drape holders
63 Baby's "piggie"

★★ Tri-Color Maze

Find the shortest path through the maze, entering at the bottom and exiting at
the top. You must pass through the color squares in this sequence: red, blue,
yellow, red, blue, etc. You may not retrace your path.

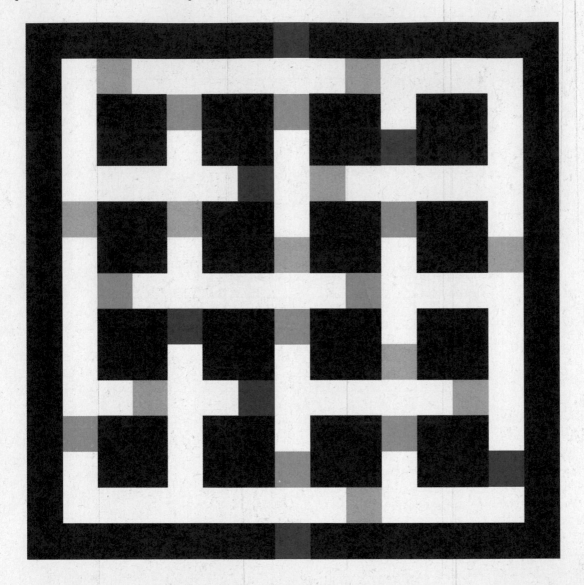

BETWEENER

What four-letter word belongs between the word at left and the word at right, so that the first
and second word, and the second and third word, each form a common two-word phrase?

SPEED __ __ __ __ DOOR

★★ Find the Ships

Determine the position of the 10 ships listed to the right of the diagram. The ships may be oriented either horizontally or vertically. A square with wavy lines indicates water and will not contain a ship. The numbers at the edge of the diagram indicate how many squares in that row or column contain parts of ships. When all 10 ships are correctly placed in the diagram, no two of them will touch each other, not even diagonally.

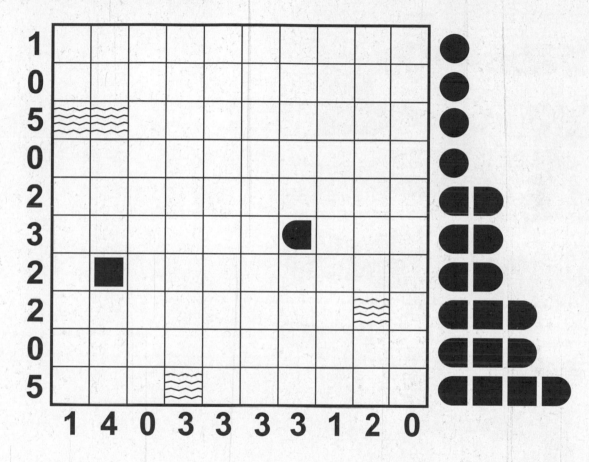

TWO-BY-FOUR

The eight letters in the word MAGAZINE can be rearranged to form a pair of common four-letter words in two different ways. Can you find both four pairs of words?

_ _ _ _   _ _ _ _

_ _ _ _   _ _ _ _

★★ Triad Split Decisions

In this clueless crossword puzzle, each answer consists of two words whose spellings are the same, except for the consecutive letters given. All answers are common words; no phrases or hyphenated or capitalized words are used. Some of the clues may have more than one solution, but there is only one word pair that will correctly link up with all the other word pairs.

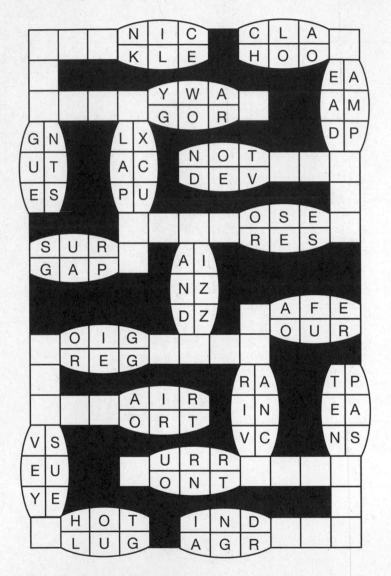

TRANSDELETION

Delete one letter from the word BLOTTIEST and rearrange the rest, to get something sharp.

_____

★★ Geometry Lesson by Doug Peterson

ACROSS

1 Forum language
6 Transcript figs.
10 Guitarist Hendrix
14 Dunne or Cara
15 Verdi title character
16 PC operator
17 Gettysburg victor
18 Goblet part
19 Forest females
20 Not relevant
23 Cassini of fashion
24 Shout out
25 Director Jean-__ Godard
26 Scandinavian capital
28 Strong suits
32 Toward the rudder
35 *Cold Case Files* network
37 Oregon's capital
38 Speaks candidly
41 Wall art
42 Taj __
43 Fr. holy woman
44 Instructive comparison
46 Quite unpleasant
48 Before, to poets
49 Clean __ whistle
50 Kuwaiti ruler
54 747, e.g.
58 Supermarket roller
59 Caesar conquest
60 Similarly
61 Gyro bread
62 On the Aegean
63 Catches some z's
64 Quartz variety
65 Clean up
66 Alfred Nobel, for one

DOWN

1 Under-the-bar dance
2 Staggering
3 Poke fun at
4 Blue dye
5 Can't do without
6 Culinary art
7 Short and sweet
8 "Zip-__-Doo-Dah"
9 Pollster's subset
10 Of courts of law
11 "Help __ the way!"
12 Athletic event
13 Treasury Dept. bureau
21 Brilliance
22 Peddle more than
27 Clipper's crew
28 Symbol of longevity
29 New Haven collegians
30 Monopoly payment
31 Hook's henchman
32 __ mater
33 Pointy-eared deity
34 Supermodel Banks
36 Genetic-code letters
39 Invoice add-on
40 Viking of comics
45 Bauble
47 Common cab color
49 Feverish symptoms
51 Indian corn
52 Affixed one's John Hancock
53 Pee Wee of baseball
54 Aspirin target
55 Bohemian
56 Cape Canaveral org.
57 Football gear
58 USN rank

★★ 123

Fill in the diagram so that each rectangular piece has one each of the numbers 1, 2, and 3, under these rules: 1) No two adjacent squares, horizontally or vertically, can have the same number. 2) Each completed row and column of the diagram will have an equal number of 1s, 2s, and 3s.

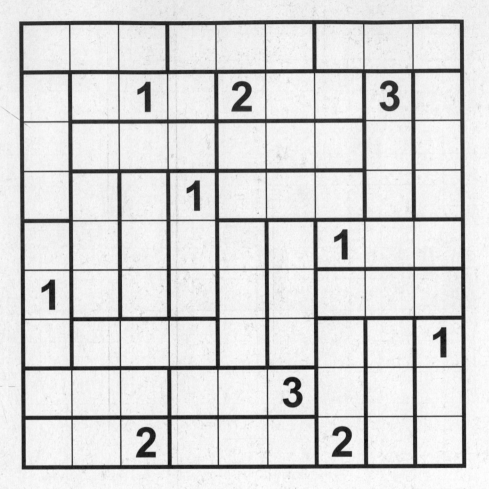

SUDOKU SUM

Without repeating any digits, complete the sum at right, by filling one digit in each of the five blanks.

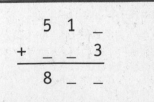

★★ Circular Reasoning

Connect all of the circles by drawing a single continuous line through every square of the diagram. All right-angle turns of your line must alternate between boxes containing a circle and boxes not containing a circle. You must make a right-angle turn out of every square that contains a circle. Your line must end in the same square that it begins, and it cannot enter any square more than once.

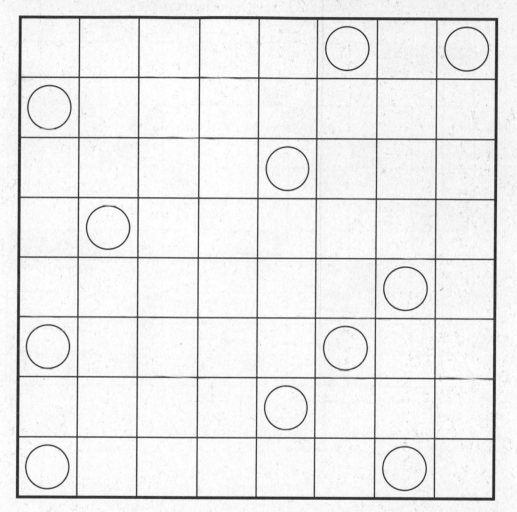

ADDITION SWITCH

Switch the positions of two of the digits in the incorrect sum at right, to get a correct sum.

```
  871
+ 267
-----
  445
```

★★ Utility Players by Fred Piscop

ACROSS

1 Lion sound
5 Fills with cargo
10 Bit of kindling
14 Seagoing predator
15 St. Theresa's town
16 Comic Carvey
17 Hayloft site
18 Pesto herb
19 Sports fig.
20 Shocking swimmer
23 Lea bleater
24 Make well
25 Like cows in India
27 University official
30 Cheerleader's prop
32 Dizzying designs
33 One of the Three Bears
34 Hatcher or Garr
37 __ Miz
38 "Dear me!"
41 Either Chaney
42 Reduced by
44 Raised, as dogs
45 Standoffish
47 Lumberjack's cry
49 Right away
50 Be serious
52 Nail remover
53 Colony insect
54 Gallery hanging, perhaps
60 Use a spoon
62 Blackmore heroine
63 Emmy winner Falco
64 *Iliad* city
65 Bugs bugs him
66 Euro fraction
67 1/1 tune word
68 Lugers' needs
69 Actor Lukas

DOWN

1 Judge's garb
2 Vocal
3 Field measure
4 Cattleman
5 Research animal
6 __ oneself of (use)
7 Frisbee, e.g.
8 Nobelist Wiesel
9 One with an order book
10 NFL scores
11 Picnic fare
12 Slack-jawed

13 Like many fences
21 Tither's donation
22 Drink like a dog
26 Shelter bed
27 Drum sound
28 Olympic sword
29 Where to fill up
30 Road-crew member
31 Essay page
33 Cut back
35 Carrot or turnip
36 Lowdown
39 Periods of decline
40 Clear wrap

43 Sermon subject
46 Not computerized, perhaps
48 "O Sole __"
49 Toolbox grippers
50 Ketch's pair
51 Logged item
52 Worked with rattan
55 Veg out
56 Apple or pear
57 Inventor's flash
58 *Pinta* partner
59 Understands
61 Reuben bread

★★ Red-Blue-Red

Enter the maze at left, pass through all the color squares once, then exit at left.
You may not retrace your path, and you may not pass through two squares of the
same color in a row.

COMMON SENSE

What four-letter word can be found in the dictionary definitions of all of these words:

BILLFOLD, TINSEL, TORTILLA, and WAFER?

— — — —

bRain BREatHer
LIFE IN OUR MELTING POT

Meeting people of different backgrounds and traveling to distant locales can have their challenges, including differences in language and culture. One thing's for sure: Whether you understand the language or not, humor *does* translate!

Boy, those French: They have a different word for everything!

—STEVE MARTIN

* * *

Touring Ireland's countryside with a group of travel writers, we passed an immaculate cemetery with hundreds of beautiful head-stones set in a field of emerald green grass. Everyone reached for their cameras when the tour guide said the inventor of the crossword puzzle was buried there. He pointed out the location, "Three down and four across."

—STEVE BAUER

* * *

Americans will put up with anything provided it doesn't block traffic.

—DAN RATHER

* * *

Our son recently married a Russian woman. During the reception, Russian and American guests proposed toasts. As some-one translated, my sister-in-law said, "Good health, good fortune. Go and multiply."

I couldn't help noticing that some of the guests looked confused. We found out later that this had been translated as, "Good health, good fortune. Go and do math."

—DAVID A. MACLEOD

Although I am of Chinese descent, I never really learned to speak Chinese. One evening, I came home boasting about a wonderful meal I'd had in Chinatown. Unfortunately, I couldn't remember the name of the restaurant, but was able to write the Chinese character that was on the door and show it to my mother.

"Do you know what it says?" Mom asked with a smile. "It says 'Pull.'"

—BARBARA MAO

* * *

The Japanese eat little fat and suffer fewer heart attacks than the British or Americans. The French eat a lot of fat and also suffer fewer heart attacks than the British or Americans. The Italians drink a lot of red wine and also suffer fewer heart attacks than the British or Americans.

Conclusion: Eat and drink what you like. Speaking English is apparently what kills you.

—IRWIN KNOPF

* * *

You can tell the ideals of a nation by its advertisements.

—NORMAN DOUGLAS

★★ Dive Right In

Find the 35 words, all at least six letters long, that contain the letters D, I, V, and E (in order, not necessarily consecutively). One of the answers is DISCOVER; the others are for you to discover. Answers include one plural ending in S.

```
Y N E C T E D R E D D E D B J D X D D F
R E Z V E K I I I G T E R A I R E M R H
E V N W I G G R S A R S C V T F I D I E
V I V O Z S E K V S V E I O I I E Q V J
I R E V O C S I D W O D V N R R V F E V
L D Z M T T T E J A E L I I I A X E W E
E W U I S C I V R N B T V V D H T T A D
D I V E A D V I D P I W E E B U R I Y E
Y E V E D N E T C V E D I V U L G E V C
T I D H I G K C E X T D E F E N S I V E
D E D S S B L N D I S R U P T I V E V I
W N V L S G E U O L E D E I I O J I Y V
W T Y O E C P J E U L A E V T I T E F E
E V I S R U C S I D B V A T I C M S R Q
V O P O V P C I O G I A P B E D F R K N
M K V Z I P S D N S S M H F J C X E Z Q
A I C S C E D I U H I P E K S Z T V L X
D S Y Y E R A L D D V D D E C I S I V E
M U N C S R E D I V I D I V I N E D V O
L E V I R D C I G Q D Y V U X D F Q L E
```

TONGUE TWISTER

From what language are all of these words derived:

AMEN, JUBILEE, BEHEMOTH, and HALLELUJAH?

A) Norwegian B) Hebrew C) Spanish D) Chinese

★★ Hyper-Sudoku

Fill in the blank boxes so that every row, column, 3x3 box, *and* each of the four 3x3 gray regions contains all of the numbers 1 to 9.

7								
		8	1		9		3	
		4	7		8			
9				7	1			
	7			2			9	
2					5		6	
	1			8				6
				9		4		1
	4						7	3

MIXAGRAMS

Each line contains a five-letter word and a four-letter word that have been mixed together (the order of the letters in each word has not been changed). Unmix the two words on each line and write them in the spaces provided. When you're done, find a two-part answer to the clue by reading down the letter columns in the answers.

CLUE: One way to China

A R O B O L S T Y = _ _ _ _ _ + _ _ _ _

T A P T O L R N Y = _ _ _ _ _ + _ _ _ _

C A M A R O U L M = _ _ _ _ _ + _ _ _ _

P A R T A W O N P = _ _ _ _ _ + _ _ _ _

★★★ Hot Stuff by Patrick Jordan

ACROSS

1 Ready for a renter
6 Put down an uprising
11 Air Force One, for one
14 Public-relations creation
15 Far from fresh
16 Tomahawk cousin
17 Camera accessory
19 Woo successfully
20 Bitter follower
21 Takes a siesta
22 Forces to flee
24 Foam in a stein
26 Speechifier's spot
28 Sign fraudulently
33 Stan's cohort
34 No longer done
35 Einstein's birthplace
37 Far partner
38 Nigeria neighbor
39 On a sloop, perhaps
40 Compass reading
41 Reef substance
42 Mrs. Ralph Kramden
43 Employ the third degree
46 Little Leaguers
47 Tarzan's neighbors
48 Rose quantity
51 Rum cake
53 Erstwhile airline
56 Sister of Zsa Zsa
57 Cold War barrier
61 No-star review
62 Chest wood
63 Physicist Mach
64 Practice, as a trade
65 __ Hawkins Day
66 Stows cargo

DOWN

1 What a splash guard protects
2 Arabian sultanate
3 One with a lot
4 Custard ingredient
5 'Twixt 12 and 20
6 Swab name
7 Caterer's coffeepots
8 Philanthropic offering
9 Sault __ Marie
10 Batgirl, e.g.
11 Spielberg's breakthrough film
12 Leave the stage
13 Sawbucks
18 Disappear slowly
23 Patriotic chant
25 Part of Ohio's border
26 *Star Trek* production company
27 Special interest grp.
28 Casual attempt
29 Puccini works
30 Grandmas, affectionately
31 Piccoloist's prop
32 Give a seat to
33 Part of BYOB
36 Ginnie __
38 Like banner headline type
39 Away from the wind
41 Instructional sessions
42 Duds
44 1956 campaign nickname
45 Actor from India
48 *Sleepy Hollow* star
49 Oat-shaped
50 Off-the-wall
51 __ B'rith
52 Tract fraction
54 Hip (to)
55 Cookout crashers
58 New Deal agcy.
59 Unpaired
60 La-la starter

★★ One-Way Streets

The diagram represents a pattern of streets. P's are parking spaces, and the black squares are stores. Find the route that starts at a parking space, passes through all stores exactly once, and ends at the other parking space. Arrows indicate one-way traffic for that block only. No block or intersection may be entered more than once.

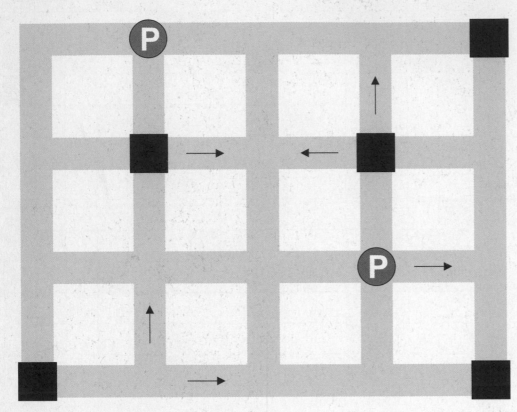

SOUND THINKING

We can think of two common uncapitalized word whose only consonant sounds are P, S, T, R, and T, in that order. How many can you think of?

_____   _____

★★ Star Search

Find the stars that are hidden in some of the blank squares. The numbered squares indicate how many stars are hidden in the squares adjacent to them (including diagonally). There is never more than one star in any square.

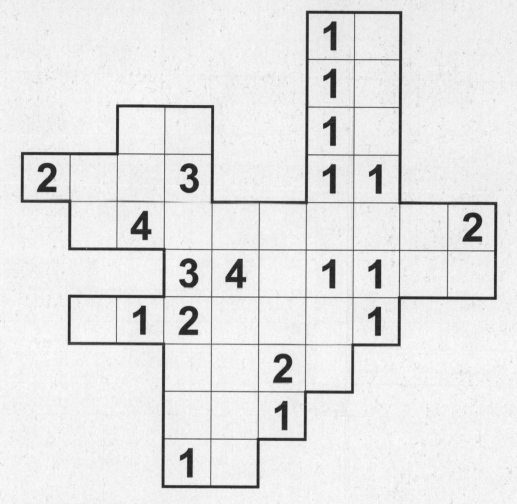

TELEPHONE TRIOS

1	ABC **2**	DEF **3**
GHI **4**	JKL **5**	MNO **6**
PRS **7**	TUV **8**	WXY **9**
*	**0**	**#**

Using the numbers and letters on a standard telephone, what three seven-letter words from the same category can be formed from these telephone numbers?

227-6228   _ _ _ _ _ _ _

496-6278   _ _ _ _ _ _ _

584-4537   _ _ _ _ _ _ _

★★★ **What a Racket** by Merle Baker

ACROSS

1 Hold back
5 Tree growth
9 Hosp. procedures
13 Fabric texture
14 N.Y. Philharmonic, for one
15 Excursion
16 Cut down
17 Raleigh's state: Abbr.
18 "We __ please"
19 Calling
22 Pa Cartwright
23 Geometric fig.
24 Graceful antelope
26 Celebrations
31 Unsullied
32 Greek letter
33 French misses
35 Puzzling problem
38 Author Rice
40 Slumber
42 Dried up
43 Actress Pola
45 Broadcast
47 Treasury Dept. division
48 Associate
50 Tells stories
52 Like a tiara
55 Bran source
56 One __ time
57 Birch beer ingredient
63 Lamenter's question
65 Himalayan legend
66 Prefix with lateral
67 Put on the books
68 Baseball star's nickname
69 Bird-feeder filler
70 Connect the __
71 Trig ratio
72 Tropical tuber

DOWN

1 Spoils
2 Roll to the runway
3 Mountaintop sign abbr.
4 Florentine family name
5 Mutts
6 Sea World attraction
7 Strikebreaker
8 Noncommittal gesture
9 __ tai
10 Roadster feature
11 Chip maker
12 Rock
15 Enliven
20 Thebes river
21 Skip over, as commercials
25 Son of Aphrodite
26 Actress Stapleton
27 Eclectic magazine
28 Type for hours on end
29 First name in scat
30 Do ushering
34 Antitoxins
36 *Harper's Bazaar* illustrator
37 Whistle blowers
39 Della's creator
41 Color changer
44 "Yeah, right!"
46 Fields expletive
49 Verily partner
51 Motionless
52 Chewed the fat
53 Word form for "nationality"
54 __ dust (uninteresting)
58 *Felicity* star Russell
59 British prep school
60 Blue hue
61 He may feed you a line
62 Former Yugoslav strongman
64 Roast hosts, for short

★★ Go With the Flow

Enter the maze at right, pass through all the stars, then exit. You must go with the flow, making no sharp turns, and may use paths more than once.

THREE AT A RHYME

Rearrange these letters to form three one-syllable words that rhyme.

A E F K K K L O O O P S

_____   _____   _____

★★ Sudoku

Fill in the blank boxes so that every row, column, and 3x3 box contains all of the numbers 1 to 9.

8	3				9	1		
		7						
			1		7		8	2
				4			1	
		5		2		7		
4	1	6		9	8			
	7			1	2			
	5			3		8		
3	9		8		4			

COUNTDOWN

Inserting plus signs and minus signs, as many as necessary, in between the digits from 9 to 1 below, create a series of additions and subtractions whose final answer is 90. Any digits without a sign between them are to be grouped together as a single number.

9   8   7   6   5   4   3   2   1   =   90

★★★ Hits and Misses by Patrick Jordan

ACROSS

1 Take hastily
5 Fields of expertise
10 Cardinal great Musial
14 *M*A*S*H* drink
15 *Our Gang* bully
16 Outburst of dread
17 Baldwin or Guinness
18 Roundup rope
19 Beseeches
20 1980 Streisand hit
23 Overtime cause
24 Free (of)
25 Film critic
27 Sauerkraut sources
32 Head off
33 End of Jack Horner's boast
34 Old-fashioned oath
36 Achieve peak flavor
39 1964 Getz/Gilberto hit, with "The"
43 Makeup merchant Lauder
44 Parasail, perhaps
45 Taste of tea
46 Basil or dill
48 Colorless liqueur
51 On the market
54 Pop artist Peter
55 One, to start with
56 1968 Beatles hit
62 Robin, vis-à-vis spring
64 __ nothings
65 Casual tops
66 Sonic replication
67 Car owner's paper
68 "Don't worry about me"
69 Prepares, as a snare
70 Hissy fits
71 Flimflams

DOWN

1 Bite like a beaver
2 Move, in real-estate lingo
3 Interrupter's sound
4 Indigestion aid, briefly
5 *Reader's Digest* staffer
6 The Parthenon, e.g.
7 List-shortening abbr.
8 Baldwin or Guinness
9 Hair-razing activities
10 Weep audibly
11 Play with Prospero
12 Ms. Dickinson
13 Snooped (around)
21 Long of *Soul Food*
22 Surplus
26 Item pulled while yelling "Whoa!"
27 Lion tamer's workplace
28 Author Kingsley
29 Item sold by Esau
30 Self-images
31 South Pacific island group
35 Anthropologist Fossey
37 Throw off
38 What a shirt collar covers
40 Goblet sediment
41 Not domesticated
42 Subjects for 35 Down
47 Thrilling times
49 Doleful
50 Alluringly different
51 Welds
52 Awaiting action
53 Land of camera fame
57 Himalayan enigma
58 Cheesy sandwich
59 Disney clownfish
60 Element #10
61 Poses, as a riddle
63 Stats.

★★★ Split Decisions

In this clueless crossword puzzle, each answer consists of two words whose spellings are the same, except for the consecutive letters given. All answers are common words; no phrases or hyphenated or capitalized words are used. Some of the clues may have more than one solution, but there is only one word pair that will correctly link up with all the other word pairs.

TRANSDELETION

Delete one letter from the word ARMENIAN and rearrange the rest, to get the two-word name of a film that won a Best Picture Academy Award.

_____   _____

★★ Islands

Shade in some of the white squares in the diagram with "water," so that each remaining white box is part of an island. Each island will contain exactly one numbered square, indicating how many squares that island contains. Each island is separated from the other islands by water but may touch other islands diagonally. All water is connected, but there are no 2x2 regions of water in the diagram.

4		3		2	
				4	
1					

AND SO ON

Unscramble the letters in the phrase SAME YAWNS, to form two words that are part of a common phrase that has the word AND between them.

_____ and _____

★★★ Sounds Like a Plan by Patrick Jordan

ACROSS

1 Croquet court
5 Necklace closer
10 Aircraft velocity unit
14 Mayberry redhead
15 1945 "Big Three" city
16 Jacob's twin
17 It's seeded and weeded
19 Lose steam
20 Pack or pick preceder
21 Freed (of)
22 Cherry "factory"
24 Comedian __ the Entertainer
26 Playback speed, briefly
27 Bank job
29 Causing a blockage
33 On one's guard
36 Layered haircut
38 Too trusting
39 Prof's preparation
40 Turbulent struggle
42 Sheet-music squiggle
43 *Men in Black* being
45 Refuse, as a request
46 Like a Granny Smith apple
47 It has a part in Exodus
49 Make sure of
51 Henry __ Lodge
53 Hook-billed bird
57 Sneaker style
60 Mincemeat treat
61 Toothpaste form
62 Sit at a stoplight
63 Inventor's setback
66 Swarm (with)
67 Conductor Leinsdorf
68 Off-white
69 Sensible
70 Camp David Accords signer
71 Markers

DOWN

1 Mr. Spock's specialty
2 Swiftly
3 Having cable TV
4 Actor Beatty
5 Trait of Dorothy Parker's writing
6 Sgt. Friday's employer
7 Without exception
8 Milkmaid's perch
9 Police routine
10 Marlon Brando, for one
11 Where India is
12 Singer Vikki
13 Colored
18 __-Lackawanna Railroad
23 "Let's go!"
25 AABBA, for one
26 Most musty
28 Storage structure
30 Arizona river
31 At any point
32 Good with one's hands
33 Have on
34 Roadster rod
35 Commando's assignment
37 Chromosome component
41 Ophthalmologist's concern
44 Nifty
48 Habitations
50 "Following that ..."
52 Phantom's milieu
54 Chilly Willy's home
55 Reeves of *Speed*
56 Cary of *The Princess Bride*
57 Web-page visits
58 Brainstorm
59 Secluded valley
60 12 points, to a printer
64 Imogene's comic cohort
65 Org. with a fingerprint file

★★ ABC

Enter the letters A, B, and C into the diagram so that each row and column has exactly one A, one B, and one C. The letters outside the diagram indicate the first letter encountered, moving in the direction of the arrow. Keep in mind that after all the letters have been filled in, there will be two blank boxes in each row and column.

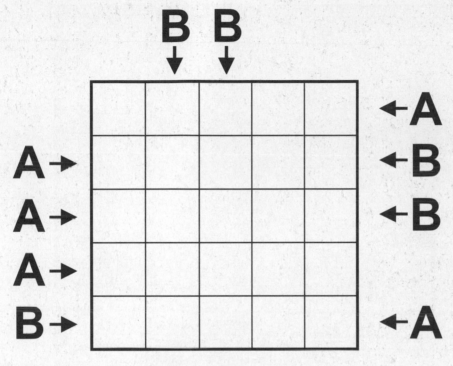

CLUELESS CROSSWORD

Complete the crossword with common uncapitalized seven-letter words, based entirely on the letters already filled in for you.

★★ Four-Letter Word Routes

Using each of the 24 letters exactly once, find the six routes that form the six
four-letter words hidden in the diagram. For each route, start with the first
letter in the word and spell the remaining letters in the word in order, by
moving through the gaps in the walls.

BETWEENER

What five-letter word belongs between the word at left and the word at right, so that the first
and second word, and the second and third word, each form a common two-word phrase?

BAD _ _ _ _ _ PIE

★★★ Line Drawing

Draw three straight lines, each from one edge of the square to another
edge, so that the Roman numerals in each of the four regions have something
in common.

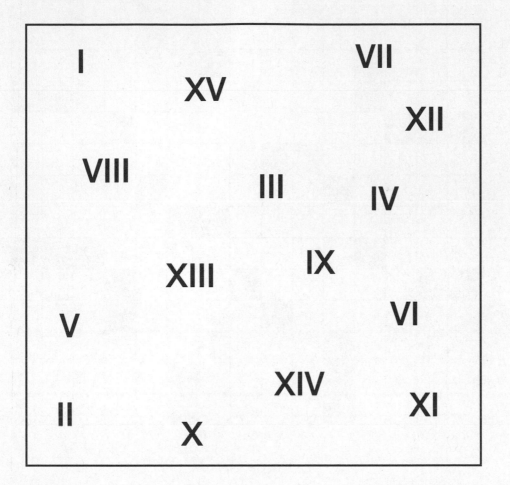

THREE OF A KIND

Find the three hidden words in the sentence that, read in order, go together in some way.

I am in doubt our government would be able to call
the Portuguese diplomat "terse."

★★★ Getting an Assist by Robert H. Wolfe

ACROSS

1 "Get lost!"
6 Small pie
10 Whaler of fiction
14 Susan Lucci role
15 Between ports
16 Female star
17 Military assistant
19 Rug coverage
20 Golf area
21 Triumphant words
22 Stakes money
24 Bobby of hockey
25 Jewel
26 Betrayed amazement
27 User
29 Little layer
32 Kitchen covering
35 Against
37 Send letters
38 Gondola mover
40 Ladd or King
41 Certain Africans
43 More than enough
44 High degree
45 Carefree venture
48 The ones there
50 Suffix meaning "sort of"
51 Use up
54 Wise Greek goddess
56 Healing plant
57 Thurman of *Pulp Fiction*
58 Neighbor of 51 Down
59 Female assistant
62 Sharp taste
63 Singer __ James
64 Rub off
65 "Us" or "Them"
66 Gang ending
67 Taste, for one

DOWN

1 Erstwhile alliance
2 Colonial announcer
3 Add-on to a bill
4 First-rate
5 *Elvira* __ (1967 film)
6 Washington city
7 __ example (for instance)
8 Sleep-stage designation
9 Drinking source
10 Old saw
11 Paid assistant
12 State confidently
13 Sheepish comments
18 Water pitcher
23 One who imitates
26 Donate
27 Riding sport
28 Tostada topping
30 Relative of etc.
31 Not any
32 To __ (unanimously)
33 Be out of breath
34 Invaluable assistant
36 "Ditto!'"
38 Book excerpts
39 Way back when
42 Boxer Spinks
43 Sticks (to)
46 Building support
47 Starting
49 Fence made of bushes
51 African nation
52 Pile up
53 Check recipient
54 New Testament book
55 Southeast Asian
56 Comic actor Johnson
60 Addams cousin
61 Strong emotion

★★ Find the Ships

Determine the position of the 10 ships listed to the right of the diagram. The ships may be oriented either horizontally or vertically. A square with wavy lines indicates water and will not contain a ship. The numbers at the edge of the diagram indicate how many squares in that row or column contain parts of ships. When all 10 ships are correctly placed in the diagram, no two of them will touch each other, not even diagonally.

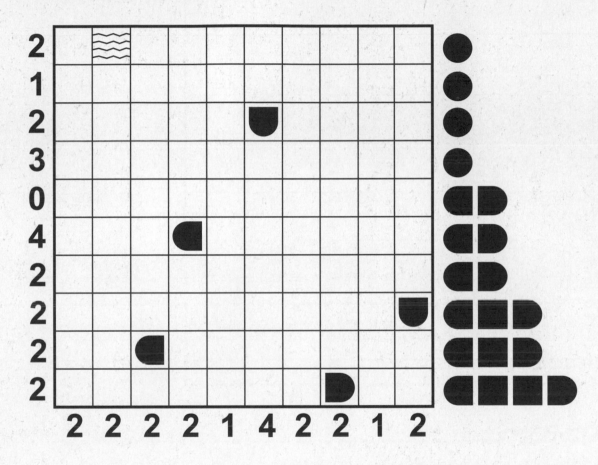

TWO-BY-FOUR

The eight letters in the word HAZELNUT can be rearranged to form a pair of common four-letter words in only one way, if no four-letter word is repeated. Can you find the two words?

— — — —   — — — —

★★★ Hyper-Sudoku

Fill in the blank boxes so that every row, column, 3x3 box, *and* each of the four
3x3 gray regions contains all of the numbers 1 to 9.

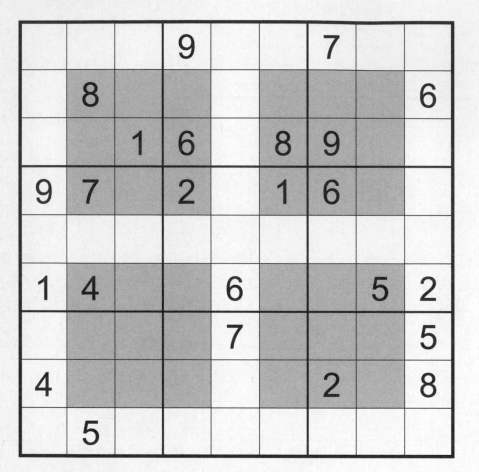

MIXAGRAMS

Each line contains a five-letter word and a four-letter word that have been mixed together (the
order of the letters in each word has not been changed). Unmix the two words on each line and
write them in the spaces provided. When you're done, find a two-part answer to the clue by
reading down the letter columns in the answers.

CLUE: Like some shows

S O A P D I S H A = _ _ _ _ _ + _ _ _ _

L U A N V I D G E = _ _ _ _ _ + _ _ _ _

P A N E G S E L T = _ _ _ _ _ + _ _ _ _

T H O R U N A Y D = _ _ _ _ _ + _ _ _ _

★★★ True Grit by Doug Peterson

ACROSS

1 Call for attention
5 Celestial sights
9 *M*A*S*H* clerk
14 Tri- times two
15 Cruise stop
16 Red Sea gulf
17 Love personified
18 Son of Isaac
19 Macaroni wheat
20 Comic-strip adventurer
23 Jazz genre
24 Ancient poet
25 Dauphin's father
27 Box-score stat
29 TV listings abbr.
30 George Foreman adversary
33 Bohemian
35 Air-quality org.
37 Hurly-burly
39 Al Capp's detective
42 Pharynx neighbor
43 Singer Zadora
44 Sushi-bar drink
45 Former JFK jet
46 White lie
48 Numbered hwy.
50 Rose home
51 Put a new handle on
53 One-fifth of MV
55 Huxley novel
59 Billiard table fabric
60 Priam's domain
61 Cork's locale
63 *Stand and Deliver* actor
64 Environmental subj.
65 Put away
66 Trouble indicator
67 Midway amusement
68 Use a keyboard

DOWN

1 Triumphant cry
2 Rope fiber
3 Much too pricey
4 Hockey great Lemieux
5 Cartel since 1960
6 Vitamin C source
7 La Scala cry
8 Bull Run general
9 Extremists
10 Waters, to Caesar
11 Fix hose
12 Sit alongside
13 Smash into

21 *All Things Considered* network
22 Chemist's attire
25 A great deal
26 Creme-filled snacks
28 Direct route
30 Good humor
31 British philosopher
32 Ticked off
34 Many mos.
36 Nile slitherer
38 TV interruptions
40 Inflatable safety device

41 Franklin stove fuel
47 Give-and-take
49 *Foucault's Pendulum* author
51 Medicine-chest item
52 Toulouse thanks
54 Helmet attachment
55 Deb's event
56 Icy coating
57 Noah of *ER*
58 Bit of rain
59 Feathery scarf
62 Fold female

★★★ Circular Reasoning

Connect all of the circles by drawing a single continuous line through every square of the diagram. All right-angle turns of your line must alternate between boxes containing a circle and boxes not containing a circle. You must make a right-angle turn out of every square that contains a circle. Your line must end in the same square that it begins, and it cannot enter any square more than once.

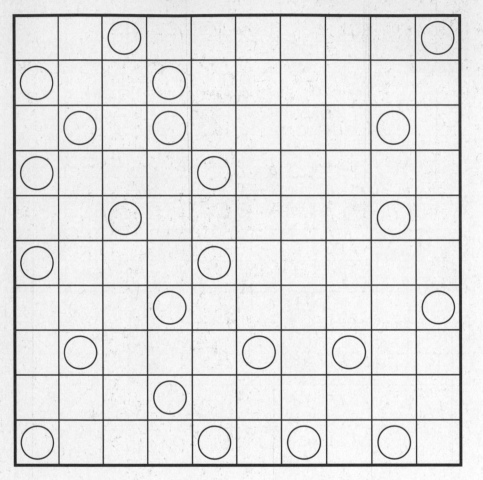

ADDITION SWITCH

Switch the positions of two of the digits in the incorrect sum at right, to get a correct sum.

$$\begin{array}{r} 631 \\ +969 \\ \hline 808 \end{array}$$

★★ Turn Maze

Entering at the bottom and exiting at the top, find the shortest path through the maze, following these turn rules: You must turn right on red squares, turn left on blue squares, and go straight through yellow squares. Your path may retrace itself and cross at intersections, but you may not reverse your direction at any point.

COMMON SENSE

What four-letter word can be found in the dictionary definitions of all of these words:

HAUL, ROAD RACING, TRAIL, and TUG OF WAR?

— — — —

★★ Islands

Shade in some of the white squares in the diagram with "water," so that each remaining white box is part of an island. Each island will contain exactly one numbered square, indicating how many squares that island contains. Each island is separated from the other islands by water but may touch other islands diagonally. All water is connected, but there are no 2x2 regions of water in the diagram.

	2				
				4	
			2		
		3			

AND SO ON

Unscramble the letters in the phrase VAIN SLOGANS, to form two words that are part of a common phrase that has the word AND between them.

_____ and _____

★★★ See Shells by Daniel R. Stark

ACROSS

1 Actor Baldwin
5 Paper size
10 Sonic bounce
14 Match a poker raise
15 Island near Venezuela
16 Author Stoker
17 Austen novel
18 Sky sight in Taurus
20 Frozen dessert
22 Auto-safety org.
23 Buddhist discipline
24 *Harvey* hero
26 Thug's blade
28 Cascades peak
31 A whole bunch
35 Chinese dynasty
36 Sgts., e.g.
38 Touch base, perhaps
39 Wildly excited
40 Rot
42 Pile on
43 Jason jilted her
45 Infuriate
46 Worry a lot
47 Raises a red flag
49 Beginners
51 Attacks, as a dog would
53 Mrs. Nick Charles
54 Equator segment
57 Easy stride
59 Passes the word to
62 Flip over
65 Gill relative
67 Bassoon cousin
68 Tighten a shoe
69 *Village Voice* award
70 Small salamander
71 Finalizes
72 Toon Le Pew

DOWN

1 Dogfight pilot
2 Easter dish
3 Ticklish Muppet
4 Casual pants
5 Gauzy insect
6 Go wrong
7 "Where America's Day Begins"
8 Eban et al.
9 Crow's-nest cry
10 Recede
11 Santa __, CA
12 Robustly healthy
13 Qatar neighbor
19 Fiat
21 __ vivant
25 Home design
27 Flattened entrée
28 Star in Orion
29 Battery terminal
30 Batman's associate
32 Playing marble
33 Renoir models
34 Eject ash
35 Doll's cry
37 Literary gathering
41 Fans
44 Slanting
48 Uses steel wool
50 High dudgeon
52 Field day
54 "This must weigh __!"
55 Cartoonist Goldberg
56 Cornfield robber
58 Kett of comics
60 Service-station job
61 Fabric sample
63 Soccer-goal material
64 __ *Abner*
66 "That's amazing!"

★★★ 123

Fill in the diagram so that each rectangular piece has one each of the numbers 1, 2, and 3, under these rules: 1) No two adjacent squares, horizontally or vertically, can have the same number. 2) Each completed row and column of the diagram will have an equal number of 1s, 2s, and 3s.

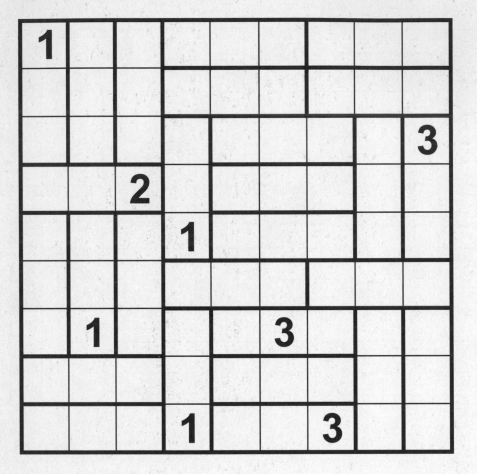

SUDOKU SUM

Without repeating any digits, complete the sum at right, by filling one digit in each of the five blanks.

```
  _ 7 _
+ 2 _ 6
_____
  _ _ 4
```

★★★ Find the Ships

Determine the position of the 10 ships listed to the right of the diagram. The ships may be oriented either horizontally or vertically. A square with wavy lines indicates water and will not contain a ship. The numbers at the edge of the diagram indicate how many squares in that row or column contain parts of ships. When all 10 ships are correctly placed in the diagram, no two of them will touch each other, not even diagonally.

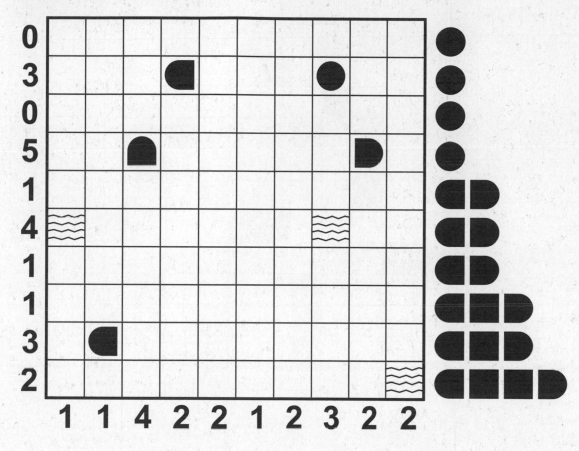

TWO-BY-FOUR

The eight letters in the word RIGHTFUL can be rearranged to form a pair of common four-letter words in only one way. Can you find the two words?

__ __ __ __   __ __ __ __

★★★ Cattle Call by Doug Peterson

ACROSS

1 Quick tug
5 Transcript stats.
9 Japanese noodles
14 K2's continent
15 Pennsylvania port
16 WWII sub
17 Drake or gander
18 Group standard
19 Mythical maiden
20 Informal discussions
23 Raw rock
24 Bowling-alley buttons
28 Katmandu resident
32 Dutch South African
34 Break bread
35 Figure skater's leap
36 Achilles tendon neighbor
39 *Inside the Third Reich* author
41 Crash sound
42 "Balderdash!"
43 Locomotive attachment
46 Painter Magritte
47 Enzyme ending
48 H. __ Perot
49 *Jeopardy!* clue
51 Land, as a fish
53 Washington's bill
54 Shy away from
61 Island near Maui
64 Earth goddess
65 Apt rhyme for "toil"
66 Social Register people
67 Small fly
68 Propel a gondola
69 Milk holder
70 Trig ratio
71 Charon's river

DOWN

1 Doorway side
2 Biblical twin
3 Small brook
4 Film critic Pauline
5 Not brand-name
6 Everyday language
7 Snootiness
8 Big rig
9 Silver-medal recipient
10 Immeasurable depth
11 Popular tattoo
12 "The Gold Bug" monogram
13 Utmost degree
21 Our sun
22 Utah city
25 Avoid
26 New Orleans university
27 Vesuvius, at times
28 Auto racers' org.
29 Bring to light
30 Reese of baseball
31 Billy Baldwin's brother
32 Doldrums
33 "All __" (Sinatra tune)
37 Basic lessons
38 Bygone political divs.
40 Some collectibles
44 Vocal quality
45 Missed the bus, perhaps
50 Society page word
52 Exams for future D.A.'s
53 Indian, for one
55 Quiche ingredients
56 Punjabi princess
57 Concert tour's load
58 Plant anchor
59 Overly suave
60 Bodybuilder's move
61 Turkey helping
62 Totally
63 Vardalos or Peeples

★★ Writers Jigsaw

The names of 32 eminent authors are arranged in jigsaw puzzle shapes in the diagram. Can you piece the puzzle together? One piece is shown to get you started.

AGATHA CHRISTIE
ALFRED, LORD TENNYSON
ARTHUR RANSOME
~~CHARLES DICKENS~~
CHARLOTTE BRONTE
DANIEL DEFOE
DOROTHY SAYERS
ERNEST HEMINGWAY
EVELYN WAUGH
GEOFFREY CHAUCER
GEORGE BERNARD SHAW

GUY DE MAUPASSANT
HENRIK IBSEN
IRIS MURDOCH
JANE AUSTEN
JOHN BETJEMAN
JOHN STEINBECK
LORD BYRON
MAEVE BINCHY
MARY WEBB
MARY WESLEY
NEVIL SHUTE

OSCAR WILDE
ROALD DAHL
ROBERT BURNS
ROBERT LOUIS STEVENSON
RUDYARD KIPLING
RUTH RENDELL
SAMUEL PEPYS
VICTOR HUGO
WALTER SCOTT
WILLIAM WORDSWORTH

```
C H A R I O R N A R T H U R R A D E L L
A M L L R G U E S B I K I R N N N U G H
E N O E I U D Y A R D K I K E S E A Y R
V E R S S H R O T C I V P C H O R W E O
E T D D M U R D W Y S J L E E M H N L B
B S B I C K E O I A N O I B R U T Y S E
I U Y R O N N C L W R H N N E V E L E R
N A E N A J S H L G U N G I M A R Y W T
C H Y L R A H C I N B S T E R E R O T L
R Y W O R O W M A I T R E B O R O O H O
A E E T D F O E G M E H T S E N D S Y U
M T B T S F C A H T A G A I W R A C S I
W N B E W R H E T U H S L L S R E Y A S
A O R B O E R S D R A N I D E E V E T S
L D H T R Y I H A P U R V G E N N B E T
T A R O A C S A S N A E E N O S H S A J
E N O F L H T W S O M B E G R O O A L E
R I E E D A I E A S E D Y U G N J M F M
S E L D D U C E N Y S Y P E P L E U R A
C O T T A H L R T N N E T D R O L D E N
```

IN OTHER WORDS

There is only one common uncapitalized word that contains the consecutive letters OSL. What's the word?

_____

★★ Bead Maze

Enter the maze at left, pass through all the beads exactly once, then exit. You
may not pass through two beads of the same color in a row.

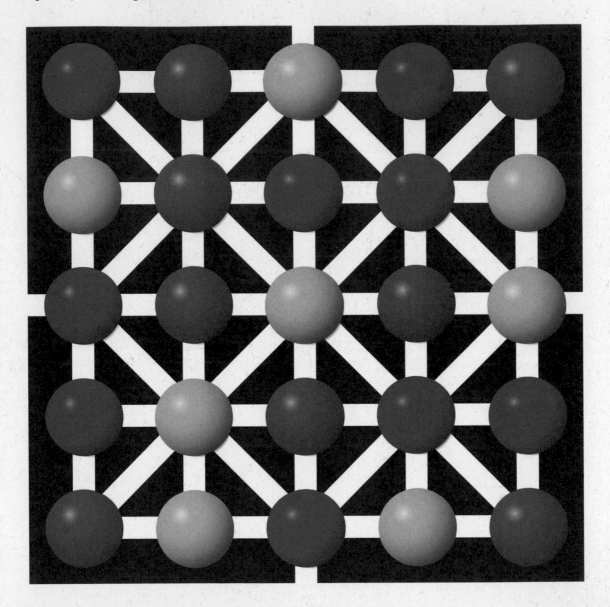

THREE AT A RHYME

Rearrange these letters to form three one-syllable words that rhyme.

A E E H I L S W W Y Y

_____ _____ _____

★★★ Star Search

Find the stars that are hidden in some of the blank squares. The numbered squares indicate how many stars are hidden in the squares adjacent to them (including diagonally). There is never more than one star in any square.

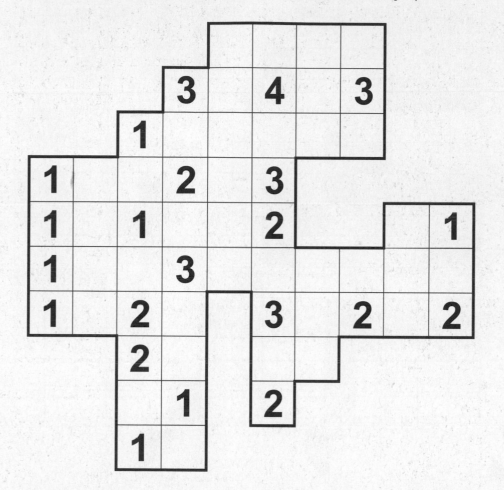

TELEPHONE TRIOS

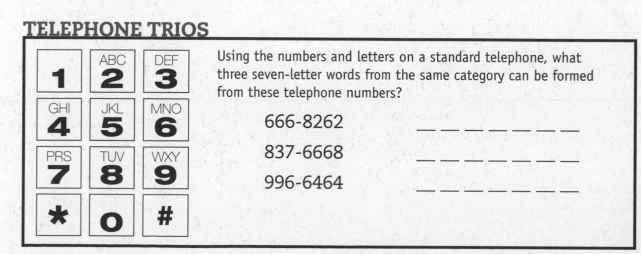

Using the numbers and letters on a standard telephone, what three seven-letter words from the same category can be formed from these telephone numbers?

666-8262   _ _ _ _ _ _ _

837-6668   _ _ _ _ _ _ _

996-6464   _ _ _ _ _ _ _

★★★ Pronounced Differences by Fred Piscop

ACROSS

1 One of a 1492 trio
6 Stud stake
10 Normandy battle site
14 Diarist Nin
15 *You Bet Your Life* host
16 Holier-than-__
17 Medicated spoonful
19 WWW addresses
20 Beef or pasta
21 75 average
22 Chucklehead
23 Ratio words
25 Grinch's creator
27 Makes a choice
30 Photo __ (campaign events)
32 Zingy taste
33 Aussie bounder
34 Russia's __ Mountains
36 Catchall category
39 Old French coins
41 Middle Ages invader
43 Light-footed
44 "Shucks!"
46 Georgetown athlete
47 Suffix with glob
48 Boaters and bowlers
50 Writer Buntline
51 Numbered rds.
52 Holy day
55 Steam up
57 River of Spain
58 CompuServe owner
60 African hot spot
64 Active one
65 Bakery machine
67 Composer __ Carlo Menotti
68 Distasteful
69 Rodeo horse
70 Sommer of film
71 "Pardon ..."
72 Mails out

DOWN

1 Running speed
2 Privy to
3 Astro ender
4 Baghdad's river
5 Campfire residue
6 Writer Tan
7 Buster with a badge
8 Made straight
9 Master hand
10 Collegians, e.g.
11 Production over time
12 Goofs off
13 Removes from power
18 Begin a journey
24 First name in talk TV
26 __ Paulo, Brazil
27 Guesser's phrase
28 Milne bear
29 "Bummer, man!"
31 Squelched
35 Plywood component
37 Perry's creator
38 Deli loaves
40 Transported by ship
42 Salad root
45 LAX listing
49 Ballparks
51 Put back to work
52 Marsh plant
53 Bubbling over
54 Moonshiner's wares
56 Babes in the woods
59 Skywalker of sci-fi
61 Nerve-cell part
62 Tear apart
63 Circle portions
66 Workout site

★★★ Sudoku

Fill in the blank boxes so that every row, column, and 3x3 box contains all of the numbers 1 to 9.

			4				3	
		7		5	3		2	6
	6				2	1		
		8		4				
9	5				1			
4	7		8					
	9			7			1	
	8	6	2		5			
	2			6			5	

MIXAGRAMS

Each line contains a five-letter word and a four-letter word that have been mixed together (the order of the letters in each word has not been changed). Unmix the two words on each line and write them in the spaces provided. When you're done, find a two-part answer to the clue by reading down the letter columns in the answers.

CLUE: Ocean motion

S E T A T H I C Y = _ _ _ _ _ + _ _ _ _

S O I K I L E R Y = _ _ _ _ _ + _ _ _ _

A R O G D U D E S = _ _ _ _ _ + _ _ _ _

M U S E H O W E R = _ _ _ _ _ + _ _ _ _

★★★ One-Way Streets

The diagram represents a pattern of streets. A and B are parking spaces, and the black squares are stores. Find the route that starts at A, passes through all stores exactly once, and ends at B. Arrows indicate one-way traffic for that block only. No block or intersection may be entered more than once.

SOUND THINKING

We can think of only one common uncapitalized word whose only consonant sounds are D, G (as in "go"), N, and S. What is the word?

_____

★★★ ABC

Enter the letters A, B, and C into the diagram so that each row and column has exactly one A, one B, and one C. The letters outside the diagram indicate the first letter encountered, moving in the direction of the arrow. Keep in mind that after all the letters have been filled in, there will be two blank boxes in each row and column.

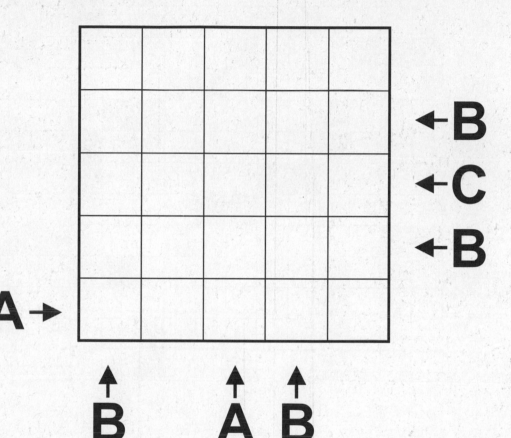

CITY SEARCH

Using the letters in JERUSALEM, we were able to form only one common uncapitalized seven-letter word, not counting plurals or verbs ending in S. Can you find the word?

— — — — — — —

★★★ The Old Sod by Robert H. Wolfe

ACROSS

1 Erstwhile rulers
6 Dick Clark, often
11 Trim bluegrass
14 Out-and-out
15 4 Seasons leader
16 Digger's find
17 It's arable
19 Gymnastics score
20 Cafeteria item
21 Really sharp
22 Very popular
23 Hippie's home
25 Addison's essay partner
27 Graduate degree requirement
30 Poland China sounds
33 Onassis, in the papers
34 Oil-rig firefighter
37 Gin flavoring
38 Drop a bit
39 Success
42 Lemon drink
43 "Farmer in the Dell" syllables
45 Sharp weapon
46 Negative connector
47 Memory pathway
50 Uses dough
52 Salad veggie
55 Affirmative vote
56 Blue billiard ball
58 Makes different
60 Main point
64 The one addressed
65 Our home
67 What Gorbachev called Reagan
68 65 Across, by another name
69 Shoulder wear
70 Like one sock
71 Type of bandage
72 Mortise's mate

DOWN

1 Bunch of hair
2 Road ending
3 Trac II alternative
4 Make a new printed copy, perhaps
5 __ Lanka
6 Big nights
7 They're upright at sea
8 Influence
9 Superior groups
10 Actress Brennan
11 Country of birth
12 Cookie of note
13 Took off
18 Affectedly genteel
24 PDQ
26 __ Alamos
27 Prepare for a future role
28 Safe place in a flood
29 Expresses an idea
31 Stirs
32 One who reads signs
33 Noted netman
35 Rhoda's mother
36 Cookout fare
40 Meal
41 Poker card
44 "Are you a man __ mouse?"
48 Makes fit
49 Fodder grass
51 Prove false
53 Beatles drummer
54 Painter Matisse
56 One new to the field
57 Golf club
59 Take in
61 Golf club
62 Battleground of 1944
63 At that time
66 CPA's quarterly tax figure

★★ Twelve-Letter Word

Using each letter in the diagram exactly once, form a twelve-letter word by starting with the first letter, and spelling the remaining letters in the word in order, by moving through the gaps in the walls.

BETWEENER

What four-letter word belongs between the word at left and the word at right, so that the first and second word, and the second and third word, each form a common two-word phrase?

LEMON __ __ __ __ CLOTH

★★★ Find the Ships

Determine the position of the 10 ships listed to the right of the diagram. The ships may be oriented either horizontally or vertically. A square with wavy lines indicates water and will not contain a ship. The numbers at the edge of the diagram indicate how many squares in that row or column contain parts of ships. When all 10 ships are correctly placed in the diagram, no two of them will touch each other, not even diagonally.

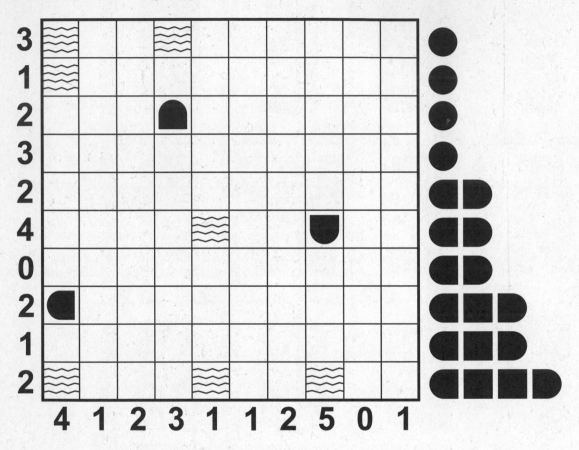

TWO-BY-FOUR

The eight letters in the word PERCEIVE can be rearranged to form a pair of common four-letter words in two different ways, if no four-letter word is repeated. Can you find both pairs of words?

_ _ _ _   _ _ _ _

_ _ _ _   _ _ _ _

★★★ 123

Fill in the diagram so that each rectangular piece has one each of the numbers 1, 2, and 3, under these rules: 1) No two adjacent squares, horizontally or vertically, can have the same number. 2) Each completed row and column of the diagram will have an equal number of 1s, 2s, and 3s.

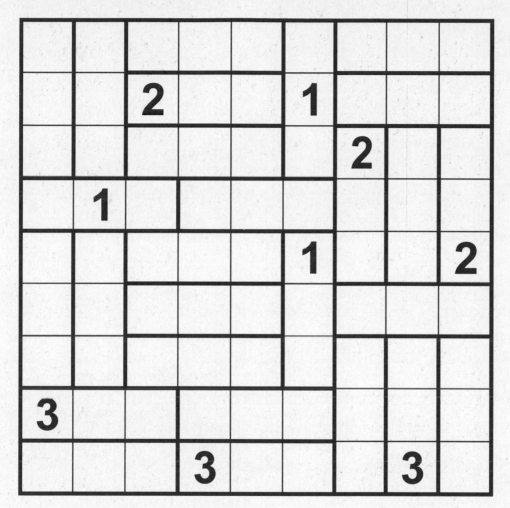

SUDOKU SUM

Without repeating any digits, complete the sum at right, by filling one digit in each of the five blanks.

```
    3  8  _
+   _  _  6
─────────────
    _  _  1
```

bRain BReatheR
LET US ENTERTAIN YOU

When it comes to film, theater, television, music, and other modes of artistic diversion, everyone's a critic. Like our favorite shows and songs, these words of wisdom run the gamut from comical to reflective:

The length of a film should be directly related to the endurance of the human bladder.

—ALFRED HITCHCOCK

Anybody can direct, but there are only eleven good writers.

—MEL BROOKS

I think most of the people involved in any art always secretly wonder whether they are really there because they're good or there because they're lucky.

—KATHARINE HEPBURN

MUSIC IS THE SOUNDTRACK OF YOUR LIFE.

—DICK CLARK

TELEVISION—A MEDIUM. SO CALLED BECAUSE IT IS NEITHER RARE NOR WELL DONE.

—ERNIE KOVACS

IF ALL THE WORLD'S A STAGE, I WANT TO OPERATE THE TRAPDOOR.

—PAUL BEATTY

It is difficult to produce a television documentary that is both incisive and probing when every twelve minutes one is interrupted by twelve dancing rabbits singing about toilet paper.

—ROD SERLING

No operatic star has yet died soon enough for me.

—THOMAS BEECHAM

Television enables you to be entertained in your home by people you wouldn't have in your home.

—DAVID FROST

An intellectual snob is someone who can listen to the "William Tell Overture" and not think of the Lone Ranger.

—DAN RATHER

★★★★ Brooklynese by Fred Piscop

ACROSS

1 Reduce to confetti
6 Woeful fellow
10 Avant-garde artist
14 Throw with effort
15 Llama land
16 Blissful state
17 Synthetic fiber
18 Diabolical
19 Story line
20 What Brooklyn tech schools do?
22 Lacoste of tennis
23 "__ to worry!'"
24 Colin Powell, once
26 Be patient
30 __ Moines, IA
31 *Garfield* pooch
32 Computer picture
36 Out of the way
40 42 Down's group
41 Gives a hoot
43 Inventor's spark
44 Banks in Cooperstown
46 Witches' brew ingredient
47 Giant, e.g.
48 Coll. transcript stat
50 Lawn neateners
52 Capitol's place
56 Small bill
57 Radiator output
58 What Brooklyn bakeries apply?
64 Opposed to
65 Fridge foray
66 Barbecue spot
67 St. Paul's architect
68 Castaway's home
69 Speechify
70 Perform a tune
71 __-do-well
72 Narratives

DOWN

1 Roe source
2 Roll-call answer
3 Talk wildly
4 "Did you __?"
5 Eleanor Roosevelt in-law
6 Shelled out
7 Strauss of jeans
8 Gasket
9 Stuck out
10 What Brooklyn dry cleaners do?
11 Psychiatrist Alfred
12 Hotelier Helmsley
13 Microchip maker
21 Column type
25 PBS supporter
26 Theological virtue
27 Garlic quality
28 MGM mascot
29 What illuminates Brooklyn stages?
33 Beans holder
34 Mine yield
35 Just out
37 Goofing off
38 Caribou, e.g.
39 Corn units
42 Shorthand pro
45 Prefix for center
49 Second man on the moon
51 Iron-fisted one
52 Melts down
53 Painter Matisse
54 Devoured
55 Renter's paper
56 Judge's demand
59 PC document
60 Mitchell mansion
61 Slanted type: Abbr.
62 Evening, in ads
63 Takes a turn

★★★ Circular Reasoning

Connect all of the circles by drawing a single continuous line through every square of the diagram. All right-angle turns of your line must alternate between boxes containing a circle and boxes not containing a circle. You must make a right-angle turn out of every square that contains a circle. Your line must end in the same square that it begins, and it cannot enter any square more than once.

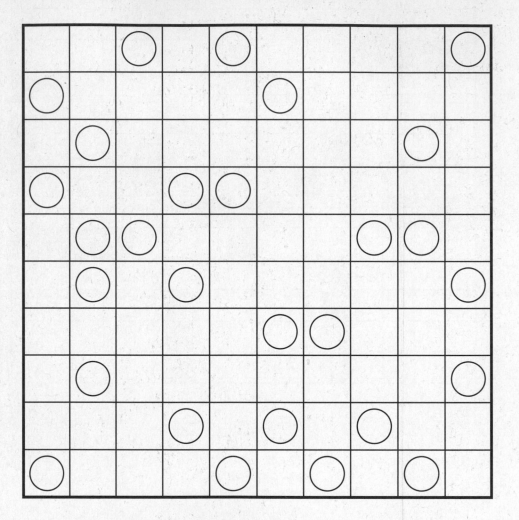

ADDITION SWITCH

Switch the positions of two of the digits in the incorrect sum at right, to get a correct sum.

$$\begin{array}{r} 598 \\ +386 \\ \hline 104 \end{array}$$

★★★ Islands

Shade in some of the white squares in the diagram with "water," so that each remaining white box is part of an island. Each island will contain exactly one numbered square, indicating how many squares that island contains. Each island is separated from the other islands by water but may touch other islands diagonally. All water is connected, but there are no 2x2 regions of water in the diagram.

2						5	
				3			
	3		4			4	
					3		
	1						1

AND SO ON

Unscramble the letters in the phrase STROLL DANCES, to form two words that are part of a common phrase that has the word AND between them.

_____ and _____

★★★★ Energy Boost by Doug Peterson

ACROSS

1 Places for pigs
6 Word on U.S. coins
11 Roll of bills
14 Cause to redden
15 Sheltered spot
16 Drugmaker Lilly
17 Eagerly anticipated chops?
19 Code-cracking org.
20 Nationality suffix
21 Chummy correspondent
22 The whole shebang
23 Backsliding
25 LAPD broadcasts
27 Fastidious monarch of rhyme?
32 Showed curiosity
35 Spanish 101 verb
36 Motown labor grp.
37 Masticate, nonstandardly
38 Aromatic ointments
40 Novel ending
41 Granola tidbit
42 Knight's protection
43 None of the above
44 Farmer's admission?
48 Relief pitcher's success
49 Back in the day
53 Catamount
55 Guiding light
58 Suit top
59 Jackie's second
60 Transylvanian cop's assignment?
62 Orchestra area
63 Beethoven title name
64 Graceful girl
65 Hearth residue
66 *Oklahoma!* aunt
67 Graf rival

DOWN

1 Clumsy one
2 Like Nero Wolfe
3 Superman's birth name
4 PC key
5 Cruised the mall
6 Surfer's milieu
7 Evel Knievel prop
8 Iris locale
9 Varnisher's supply
10 Big bang maker
11 Took a turn for the worse
12 In addition
13 *Charlie's Angels* actress
18 Desert bluff
22 Leading letters
24 Once more
26 Org. for Els
28 Shade of green
29 School of thought
30 Past the deadline
31 Washstand pitcher
32 "Don't have __!"
33 Peacock Throne occupant
34 "God Bless America" singer
38 Ken Burns miniseries
39 Use a sight
40 Summers on the Seine
42 Basic cable offering
43 Meditator's goal
45 Small battery size
46 More frilly
47 Borodin prince
50 __ *for Adano*
51 Soda flavor
52 Blue language
53 Storybook bear
54 *Exodus* author
56 Oscar winner Jannings
57 Basilica section
60 Flight formation
61 "Later!"

★★ Tri-Color Maze

Find the shortest route through the maze, entering at the bottom and exiting at the top. You must pass over the color sections in this sequence: red, blue, yellow, red, blue, etc. Change colors by passing through a white square. It is okay to retrace your path.

BETWEENER

What five-letter word belongs between the word at left and the word at right, so that the first and second word, and the second and third word, each form a common two-word phrase?

COLOR __ __ __ __ __ DOG

★★★ Hyper-Sudoku

Fill in the blank boxes so that every row, column, 3x3 box, *and* each of the four 3x3 gray regions contains all of the numbers 1 to 9.

4	2					1		
		8					2	
6		7	9			3		
	6	4				9		
	8						7	
		9	1				6	
	3		5		9			
7				1				
						2	8	

MIXAGRAMS

Each line contains a five-letter word and a four-letter word that have been mixed together (the order of the letters in each word has not been changed). Unmix the two words on each line and write them in the spaces provided. When you're done, find a two-part answer to the clue by reading down the letter columns in the answers.

CLUE: Toddler's train

A S C A C R E S E	=	_ _ _ _ _	+	_ _ _ _
W H A H O M E A D	=	_ _ _ _ _	+	_ _ _ _
V O F O G U X E Y	=	_ _ _ _ _	+	_ _ _ _
G O D O I O L F Y	=	_ _ _ _ _	+	_ _ _ _

★★ "P" as in "Puzzle"

All these 10-letter words starting with the letter P can be found in P shapes in the diagram. One word is shown to get you started.

```
S U C H U T E C E J G E R T O F P E C H
H O N K I L U T H O R S I W I K S U T I
I P I N W L R I P R O A N E R I O S U O
O L B I R E B L L O W C K P E L R C T N
N A R A I N T E P R G Y L G O L P H M I
J Y E P C R E P R O T A E P R E L U T E
T A T S E M I P I U P L O O N O F O R T
N N I N T I P E W N W A R B A N G R O T
A N O I A L K N I D N Y E L C A E T F I
L A T O R L O G R U O R P S K I W B T N
P L O C P R T I A R A C A O W P M R W I
E A S R E C O H P T E T P L N C I U P A
P T P E R U H E L O R O T S I A N S H R
P O S H I W P N K R B A C K P S T H G A
E R T U H O O J E P A P E L E R M I L L
A L O T S A T E S N R C H U P G I W O L
T J O E A R E T H I K A F T P T N C I L
N S N S E U S T P O S R S E E J O A P I
A T I O P R H I L L M A F O P T E S N Y
P A I N T B C A N T A P R O T R A E T S
```

PAINKILLER
PAINTBRUSH
PANTALOONS
PAPERBACKS
PARACHUTES
PEASHOOTER
PEPPERMILL
PEPPERMINT
PERCOLATOR
PERIWINKLE
PHOTOGRAPH
PIANOFORTE
PILLOWCASE
PINCUSHION
PLANTATION
PLAYGROUND
POINSETTIA
PROJECTILE
PROSPECTUS
PROTRACTOR

INITIAL REACTION

The "equation" below contains the initials of words that will make it correct, forming a numerical fact. Solve the equation by supplying the missing words.

1 = W. on a U. _____

★★★★ Common Cents by Merle Baker

ACROSS

1 Matter at hand
6 Italian wine region
10 Collars
14 Literary device
15 It might be stubbly
16 Nastase of tennis
17 Over-the-counter trade
19 Drain problem
20 Sauce source
21 Was beholden to
22 Crazy Horse, for one
24 Dorm neighbor, perhaps
25 Vitamin partner
26 Quantity
29 Place for instruments
30 Change the price on
31 Be tenacious
35 __ about (roughly)
36 Parts of faces
37 Bond film
38 Bit of dirt
40 Horne and Olin
41 Chair designer
42 Perches
43 Medical treatment
46 Stay away from
47 Moniker
48 Decorative pitcher
49 Naval noncom
52 Shivering fit
53 Garden-variety
56 DEA operative
57 Enthusiastic
58 Wipe clean
59 Arduous journey
60 Mediterranean port
61 Varieties

DOWN

1 Bistro-table leavings
2 Black-and-white treat
3 Kid's ride
4 Homey hostel
5 1937 Cooperstown selection
6 Didn't procrastinate
7 Not barefoot
8 Quirk
9 Hints
10 Old-time theater
11 __ nothing
12 Life of a region
13 *Who's Afraid of Virginia Woolf?* actor
18 Big blow
23 Work without __
24 Ship level
25 Not boyish
26 Baseball star's nickname
27 Waiter's offering
28 Nebraska Indians
29 Dupes
31 Affectionate appellation
32 Coffee vessels
33 Small fly
34 Cartwright son
36 Accepted eagerly
39 False god
40 French pilgrimage site
42 Ostrich relative
43 Hammarskjöld follower
44 Comic strip Viking
45 Toughen
46 Bergman, by birth
48 Mideast bigwig
49 Autocrat
50 Annoyance
51 Change for a five
54 Wall climber
55 Spanish gold

★★ Triad Split Decisions

In this clueless crossword puzzle, each answer consists of two words whose spellings are the same, except for the consecutive letters given. All answers are common words; no phrases or hyphenated or capitalized words are used. Some of the clues may have more than one solution, but there is only one word pair that will correctly link up with all the other word pairs.

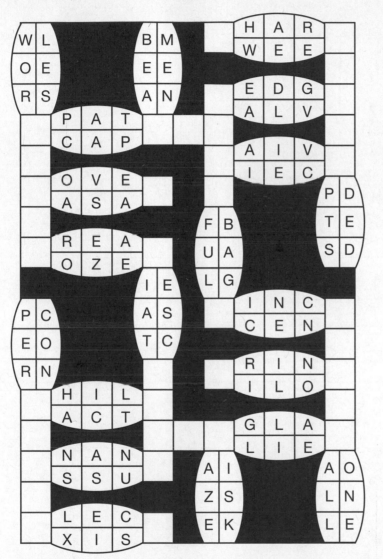

TRANSDELETION

Delete one letter from the word ANOINTMENTS and rearrange the rest, to get a term for a resident of a certain U.S. state.

_____

★★★ One-Way Streets

The diagram represents a pattern of streets. A and B are parking spaces, and the black squares are stores. Find the route that starts at A, passes through all stores exactly once, and ends at B. Arrows indicate one-way traffic for that block only. No block or intersection may be entered more than once.

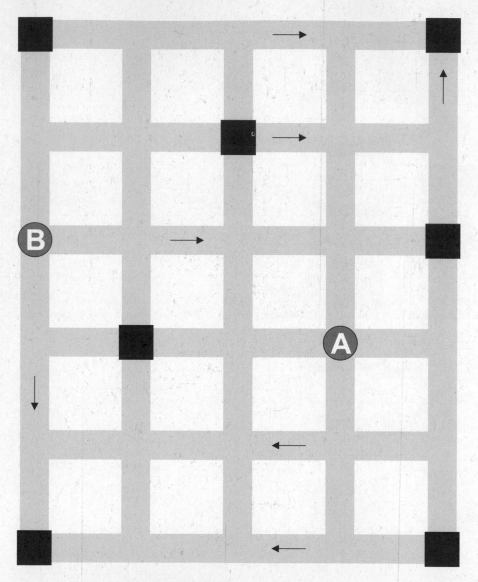

SOUND THINKING

We can think of two common uncapitalized words whose only consonant sounds are N, L, and J, in that order. How many can you think of?

_____   _____

★★★★ How Easy Is It? by Richard Silvestri

ACROSS

1 Tunes that chart
5 Piece of property
9 Palindrome starter
14 Soothsayer's sighting
15 Bit of bank business
16 Puff up
17 Word from Mork
18 Galoot
19 Balance in the air?
20 Baltimore goodies
22 Implied
23 Poisonous herb
24 Come together
25 Muppet Emmet
26 Changed the décor
29 Down with a bug
32 Jones' partner
34 Kind of stock option
35 Corporate VIP
36 Be 29 Across
39 Barbara of *Dr. Quinn, Medicine Woman*
42 Cap'n Crunch competitor
43 Brothers' title
44 No-seats sign
45 Half a bray
47 Bar bill
48 Washington, for one
50 Rectangular piers
54 Manitoba Indian
56 Drink with paella
58 Flatware item
60 Unit of electricity
62 At __ (in any case)
63 Move toward
64 __ *dixit*
65 Fall flower
66 Hung onto
67 Nautical pole
68 Sphagnous
69 Geometric calculation
70 Red-__ (cinnamon candy)

DOWN

1 Big shot
2 Turkish inn
3 Rent payer
4 Ignored
5 Composer Berg
6 Kitchen appliance
7 Level to the ground
8 Slaughter in Cooperstown
9 Got all gooey
10 Smith, perhaps
11 Small diving bird
12 Abruzzi bell town
13 Substantial content
21 Chocolate substitute
24 "Sing Along" Miller
27 Orlando-area attraction
28 Couple
30 Oahu souvenir
31 Smoked salmon
33 Refuse
36 Toward the tail
37 Tax shelter
38 What some scientists wear
40 Bikini top
41 Reeves of film
46 Part of ESL
48 Watchword requester
49 Get away
51 Allegro non __
52 Draws a bead on
53 Cavalry weapons
55 Valentine bouquet
57 It comes from the heart
58 Criticize
59 Colombian coin
60 "My Way" lyricist
61 Keg serving

★★ Dicey

Group the dice into 12 sets of three, with each set having a sum of 11. The three dice in each set must be connected to each other by a common horizontal or vertical side.

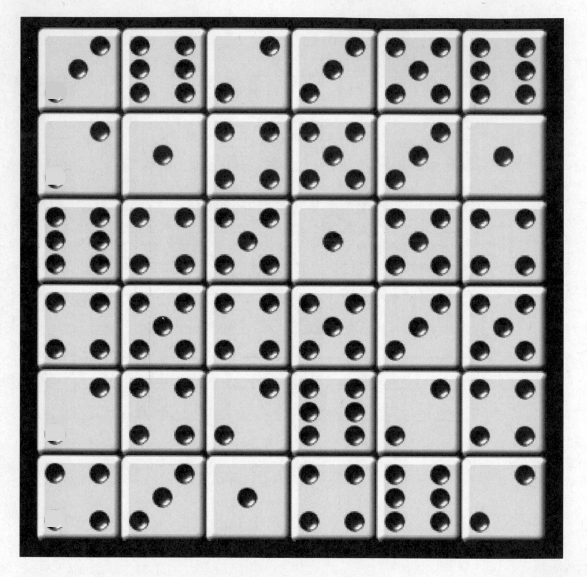

COMMON SENSE

What five-letter word can be found in the dictionary definitions of all of these words:

ACCOUNTING, CENSOR, OLD TESTAMENT, and SCHOOLBAG?

— — — — —

★★★ Star Search

Find the stars that are hidden in some of the blank squares. The numbered squares indicate how many stars are hidden in the squares adjacent to them (including diagonally). There is never more than one star in any square.

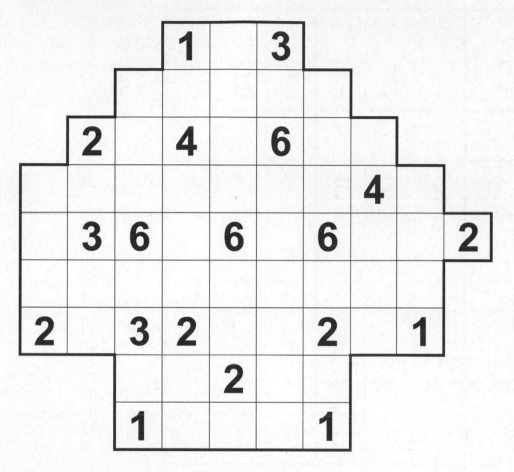

TELEPHONE TRIOS

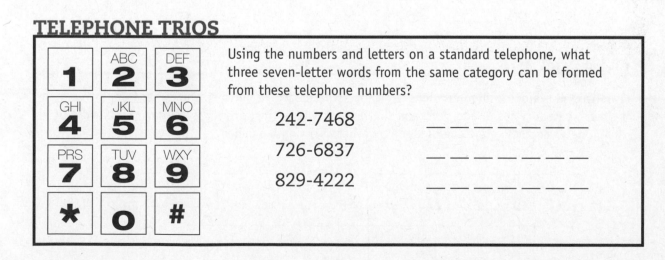

Using the numbers and letters on a standard telephone, what three seven-letter words from the same category can be formed from these telephone numbers?

242-7468   _ _ _ _ _ _ _

726-6837   _ _ _ _ _ _ _

829-4222   _ _ _ _ _ _ _

★★★ Sudoku

Fill in the blank boxes so that every row, column, and 3x3 box contains all of the numbers 1 to 9.

			9					
	1			6		3	5	
							1	
7			2	5	6			4
	6		8				7	
5		4					8	6
					5			
2			3	8				
3	9			7		2	4	

COUNTDOWN

Inserting plus signs and minus signs, as many as necessary, in between the digits from 9 to 1 below, create a series of additions and subtractions whose final answer is 29. Any digits without a sign between them are to be grouped together as a single number.

9 8 7 6 5 4 3 2 1 = 29

★★★★ Drive Line by Patrick Jordan

ACROSS

1 Leave at the altar
5 "Get out of here!"
9 It's rattled in battle
14 Concept
15 Hospital section
16 J.R. Ewing's mother
17 Beethoven's birthplace
18 To boot
19 Make up (for)
20 This puzzle's subject
23 Source of the Clampett fortune
24 Biol. or geol.
25 Supermarket freebie
28 Mike Brady and Homer Simpson
31 Curiosity-piquing ad
36 WWW search results
38 Franklin flew one
40 Barbershop request
41 Start of a 20 Across
44 Shinbone
45 Rain-delay coverup
46 Relax restrictions
47 Completed
49 Turn a __ ear
51 Trough site
52 Ram's remark
54 Sine __ non
56 End of a 20 Across
65 English earldom
66 Gift wrapper's roll
67 Third World locale
68 Skirt style
69 Airline serving Israel
70 Madcap
71 Military stations
72 Hinge (on)
73 Supplements, with "out"

DOWN

1 Three-sided sails
2 Admired one
3 *If Roast Beef Could Fly* author
4 Dance with dips
5 Tchaikovsky masterpiece
6 5, to 10
7 Approximately
8 Nose-wrinkling stimuli
9 Squalid to the max
10 Saxophone range
11 Rorschach image
12 Stuttgart article
13 Film spool
21 First or foreign follower
22 Do something
25 Exceeds 21, in blackjack
26 Bandleader Shaw
27 Geographer's sphere
29 Motocross track's surface
30 Lieu
32 Skipper of the *Pequod*
33 "__ alive!"
34 Olympics contest
35 All set
37 *Wheel of Fortune* turn
39 Raison d'__
42 Where derbies may be held
43 In an unclear manner
48 Clumsy sort
50 Astor's stock in trade
53 On the trail of
55 Dumbfound
56 Bring in the harvest
57 Norway's largest city
58 Without a guarantee
59 Slight progress
60 "Boola Boola" school
61 14th anniversary gift
62 Writer Dinesen
63 With 64 Down, novena's length
64 See 63 Down

★★★ ABC

Enter the letters A, B, and C into the diagram so that each row and column has exactly one A, one B, and one C. The letters outside the diagram indicate the first letter encountered, moving in the direction of the arrow. Keep in mind that after all the letters have been filled in, there will be two blank boxes in each row and column.

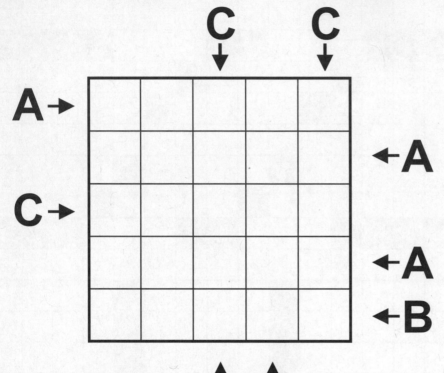

CLUELESS CROSSWORD

Complete the crossword with common uncapitalized seven-letter words, based entirely on the letters already filled in for you.

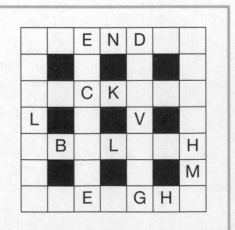

★★★ Find the Ships

Determine the position of the 10 ships listed to the right of the diagram. The ships may be oriented either horizontally or vertically. A square with wavy lines indicates water and will not contain a ship. The numbers at the edge of the diagram indicate how many squares in that row or column contain parts of ships. When all 10 ships are correctly placed in the diagram, no two of them will touch each other, not even diagonally.

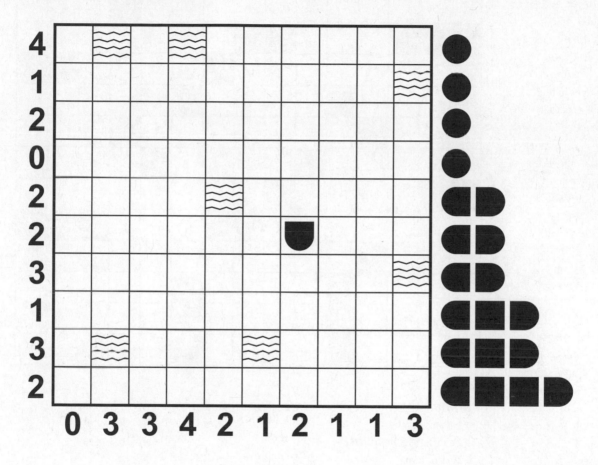

TWO-BY-FOUR

The eight letters in the word VILLAINY can be rearranged to form a pair of common four-letter words in only one way. Can you find the two words?

— — — —   — — — —

★★★★ Dejected by Merle Baker

ACROSS

1 Impudent
6 Shakers, e.g.
10 Like some chances
14 Words to live by
15 Cowardly Lion portrayer
16 Orderly
17 __ a time
18 Droxie alternative
19 Aid in wrongdoing
20 Political humor?
23 Stadium shout
24 Cover
25 Rises precipitously
27 Italian sports car
32 At any time
33 Fly-ball paths
34 Circle dance
36 Pharaoh's land
39 "Uh-uh!"
40 Easy-listening station policy?
42 Corp. VIP
43 Run off together
45 Sort of seaweed
46 In the rear
47 Directional starter
49 Rich courses
51 Fountain treats
54 Break bread
55 Recede
56 Laurel in a courtroom?
62 Wind around
64 Not written
65 Give shelter to
66 Track shape
67 Sidewalk edge
68 James Blake's nickname
69 Pianist Peter
70 Community pool site
71 Home or bed ending

DOWN

1 Campus VIP
2 Barrett of Hollywood
3 "Up and __!"
4 Cupboard contents
5 Balderdash
6 Toil wearily
7 Bring home
8 Culinary masters
9 Actors on the road
10 RR depot
11 Bookmobile?
12 Something to shoot for
13 Folk tales
21 Snake River state
22 The Pink Panther actor
26 Long or short alternative: Abbr
27 Chestnut hair
28 Asian sea
29 University of Arkansas mascot?
30 Clock sound
31 Rubbed the wrong way
35 Competent
37 Locust, for one
38 Preschoolers
40 Extend, in a way
41 Church areas
44 Outlay: Abbr
46 Discloses
48 Folly
50 Beauty pageant wear
51 Breakfast fruit
52 Over
53 Play a banjo
57 DEA agent
58 Napoleon exile site
59 Toothpaste holder
60 Home to billions
61 Have to have
63 UN observer grp.

★★ Blue-Red-Blue

Enter the maze at the bottom, pass through all the color squares once, then exit at the top. You may not retrace your path, and you may not pass through two squares of the same color in a row.

THREE AT A RHYME

Rearrange these letters to form three one-syllable words that rhyme.

A A C E E E H I P P P R R S S S T

_____ _____ _____

★★★ 123

Fill in the diagram so that each rectangular piece has one each of the numbers 1, 2, and 3, under these rules: 1) No two adjacent squares, horizontally or vertically, can have the same number. 2) Each completed row and column of the diagram will have an equal number of 1s, 2s, and 3s.

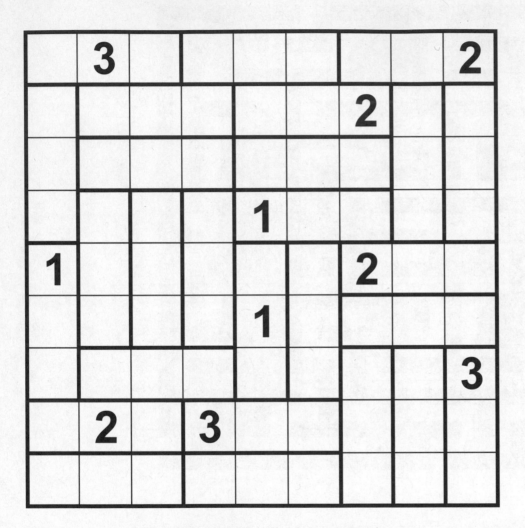

SUDOKU SUM

Without repeating any digits, complete the sum at right, by filling one digit in each of the five blanks.

$$
\begin{array}{r}
\_\ \_\ 4 \\
+\ \ 1\ \ 7\ \ \_ \\
\hline
6\ \ \_\ \ \_
\end{array}
$$

★★★ Circular Reasoning

Connect all of the circles by drawing a single continuous line through every square of the diagram. All right-angle turns of your line must alternate between boxes containing a circle and boxes not containing a circle. You must make a right-angle turn out of every square that contains a circle. Your line must end in the same square that it begins, and it cannot enter any square more than once.

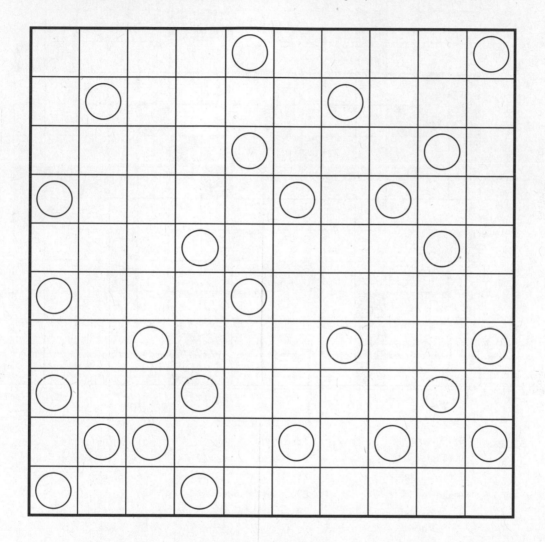

ADDITION SWITCH

Switch the positions of two of the digits in the incorrect sum at right, to get a correct sum.

```
  1 7 6
+ 2 3 5
-------
  9 1 6
```

★★★★ Middle Management by Fred Piscop

ACROSS

1 Arens or Dayan
6 Chance to hit
11 Chucklehead
14 Ill-looking
15 Nary a soul
16 Frazier foe
17 Large Vegas hotel
19 Beehive State Indian
20 Crumpets partner
21 Yell "Rah!"
22 Greek vowels
24 Gobble up
25 The Braves, on scoreboards
26 "__ the Top"
28 Hold on tight
33 Cartoon unit
34 Reveal, in poetry
35 First chip
36 Bergen dummy
39 Live and breathe
40 *Golf Begins at Forty* author
41 Evergreen-scented
42 Grounded Aussie
43 Prefix for center
44 Eat forbidden fruit, perhaps
48 Buenos __
49 Bruins great
50 Road warning
53 On or about
55 Gets on the ump
56 Post-ER place
57 Director Lee
58 Bribe offerer
62 Mineral suffix
63 Search for prey
64 Took an oath
65 __'easter
66 Wipe clean
67 In knots

DOWN

1 Paint finish
2 Milo or Tessie
3 Sword holder
4 Clothing line
5 Like some invitations
6 Luanda's land
7 Wrongful act
8 Jungle crusher
9 Author Beattie
10 Ennui
11 Sweet wine
12 Utah ski site
13 Pizzeria orders
18 Traveler's stop
23 Like some produce
26 "Holy cow!"
27 Seam discovery
29 Kind of paint
30 Discussion venue
31 Call __ day
32 __ XING
36 Sunblock letters
37 Actress Vardalos
38 Photo-lab gadget
39 Tori of pop
40 Least dense
42 Bard's "before"
43 Gaffe
45 Frozen dessert
46 Internet IPO of '04
47 Stock-ticker inventor
51 Pastry prettifiers
52 Reduce to mush
53 Genesis son
54 Divider's word
55 Autobahn autos
59 Flight board abbr.
60 Mauna __
61 Leave floored

★★★ Hyper-Sudoku

Fill in the blank boxes so that every row, column, 3x3 box, *and* each of the four 3x3 gray regions contains all of the numbers 1 to 9.

1		8			7			2
2	7							
3						4		
		3		8				
	9			4				
		4		7	6	2	5	
				2				6
				1	3			5
5				9				

MIXAGRAMS

Each line contains a five-letter word and a four-letter word that have been mixed together (the order of the letters in each word has not been changed). Unmix the two words on each line and write them in the spaces provided. When you're done, find a two-part answer to the clue by reading down the letter columns in the answers.

CLUE: Salt's shade

N A B O V U E L T = _ _ _ _ _ + _ _ _ _

P A G L O N U G Y = _ _ _ _ _ + _ _ _ _

V I D U C A N E R = _ _ _ _ _ + _ _ _ _

Y I M E R E L E D = _ _ _ _ _ + _ _ _ _

★★★ Split Decisions

In this clueless crossword puzzle, each answer consists of two words whose spellings are the same, except for the consecutive letters given. All answers are common words; no phrases or hyphenated or capitalized words are used. Some of the clues may have more than one solution, but there is only one word pair that will correctly link up with all the other word pairs.

TRANSDELETION

Delete one letter from the word ENTRANCE and rearrange the rest, to get something you might take on a camping trip.

_____

★★★★ Impact Statements by Merle Baker

ACROSS

1 Rough it
5 Hackneyed
10 Police alerts
14 *Inter __*
15 Mah-jongg pieces
16 Clever remark
17 Risky purchase
19 Golden Rule word
20 Assembly-line workers
21 "Milk" word form
22 Reflexive pronoun
25 One in a hurry
26 Business card abbr.
27 Right hook answer, perhaps
30 Abbr. in apt. ads
31 First name in country
33 '60s portrayer of the Joker
35 Hubbubs
36 Rugged rocks
38 Poet's foot
41 Prepare quickly
43 Harris term of address
44 Work unit
46 Places for some stickers
50 Genetic material
51 Fretfulness
53 Lottery winner's option
55 Mountaineer's tool
56 Naval builder
58 Kicker's target
59 Cowboy's device
63 Ponder
64 Be in line (with)
65 Diamond shape
66 Mimics
67 Title pages
68 Talks and talks and talks and talks and ...

DOWN

1 Limit
2 2001 biopic
3 Russian fighter
4 Ice skating event
5 Not volatile
6 Court start
7 Heaps
8 Albanian coins
9 Language ending
10 Blue hues
11 Gambling devices
12 Resentful
13 Wild animal tracks
18 Yuletide tune
21 Garage job
22 Other, in Oaxaca
23 Call for
24 Effort
25 Ewes' mates
28 *The Sound of Music* family name
29 Exercise run
32 Bat wood
34 Umbrella part
36 PC necessities
37 Jamaican liquor
39 Carte
40 Writer Stoker
42 Wild goat
44 It's inexplicable
45 Make up
47 Overjoyed
48 Moscow moola
49 Hook helper
52 Bucolic hollows
54 Energetic
56 Like some advice
57 To be, in Haiti
59 Scoundrel
60 New Deal agcy.
61 Furniture wood
62 Hosp. personnel

★★★ Brain Coral Maze

Find the longest continuous loop in the picture. Your path may not enter the blue areas outside the circle.

BETWEENER

What five-letter word belongs between the word at left and the word at right, so that the first and second word, and the second and third word, each form a common two-word phrase?

TAXI __ __ __ __ __ PAT

★★★ Islands

Shade in some of the white squares in the diagram with "water," so that each remaining white box is part of an island. Each island will contain exactly one numbered square, indicating how many squares that island contains. Each island is separated from the other islands by water but may touch other islands diagonally. All water is connected, but there are no 2x2 regions of water in the diagram.

			4				
		1					
	3		3				
					5		
1				4			
	4						

AND SO ON

Unscramble the letters in the phrase THWARTS ROARING, to form two words that are part of a common phrase that has the word AND between them.

_____ and _____

★★★ One-Way Streets

The diagram represents a pattern of streets. A and B are parking spaces, and the black squares are stores. Find the route that starts at A, passes through all stores exactly once, and ends at B. Arrows indicate one-way traffic for that block only. No block or intersection may be entered more than once.

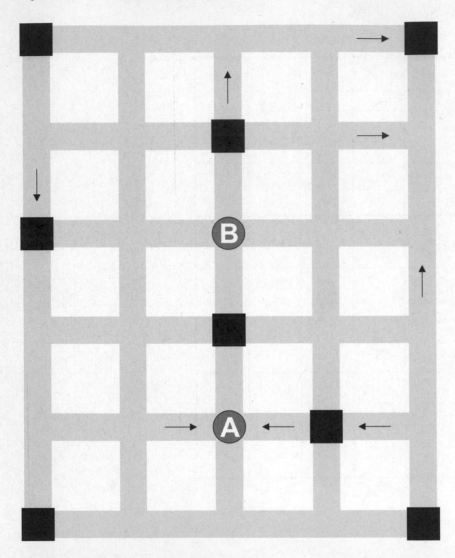

SOUND THINKING

The consonant sounds in the word FRANCE are F, R, N, and S. We can think of two common uncapitalized words whose only consonant sounds are also F, R, N, and S, in that order. How many can you think of?

_____   _____

★★★★ Hi, Sweetie by Ann W. Masten

ACROSS

1 Early 9th-century date
5 Brewer's buy
9 Command to Fido
14 Sleep, so to speak
15 Author Wiesel
16 Designer Ashley
17 Erupter of 1991
18 Management level
19 "Good __!"
20 *Blondie* daughter
23 Sweetie
24 __ polloi
25 A thing's
26 Moral error
28 Atm- relative
29 __-cone
30 Deserve
31 Microscopic creature
34 Asian respectful title
35 Burn soother
36 '80s middleweight champ
39 Georgia and Armenia, formerly: Abbr.
40 Beehive State athletes
41 Like some detergents
42 Fit to __
43 Marie's sea
44 Fall guy
45 Diplomat Hammarskjöld
46 "Washboard" muscles
47 "I'm frightened!"
48 Balk caller
51 Barbara Bain, in *Mission: Impossible*
55 Do cinematography
56 Division word
57 Coin in Helsinki
58 Deploy again
59 Numerical suffix
60 Edge
61 Beasts of burden
62 Intently
63 Apartment pests

DOWN

1 Havel's native language
2 "Likewise!"
3 Noble gas
4 Karen's pen name
5 Crater creator
6 Legal defense
7 Stead
8 Anodes and cathodes
9 Some shoes
10 Serenity
11 Sandwich filler
12 Ones with IOUs
13 Hem partner
21 "__ America Singing"
22 Symbol of inflexibility
27 Not loaded
28 Bring down
29 Not as forward
30 Accumulated
31 Syrian leader
32 Milk drinkers' mementos
33 Flagrant
34 "God Bless America" introducer
37 Ballroom dance
38 1970 World's Fair locale
44 Short time
46 Pennies, at times
47 Go forward
48 Go back
49 Deserve
50 Limo destinations
52 Wine aroma
53 Draft rating
54 WB sitcom
55 Sp. woman

★★★ Sudoku

Fill in the blank boxes so that every row, column, and 3x3 box contains all of the numbers 1 to 9.

7		9	5					
5					1			8
		4		6		1		
						2	4	
3				2	4	9		
								7
		6						4
1		5				6	8	9
2			8				7	

MIXAGRAMS

Each line contains a five-letter word and a four-letter word that have been mixed together (the order of the letters in each word has not been changed). Unmix the two words on each line and write them in the spaces provided. When you're done, find a two-part answer to the clue by reading down the letter columns in the answers.

CLUE: Stocking stuffer

A L B E F I D E T = _ _ _ _ _ + _ _ _ _

K O D A P O U R T = _ _ _ _ _ + _ _ _ _

B A R L I S O B E = _ _ _ _ _ + _ _ _ _

P E M A N T H A L = _ _ _ _ _ + _ _ _ _

★★★ Star Search

Find the stars that are hidden in some of the blank squares. The numbered squares indicate how many stars are hidden in the squares adjacent to them (including diagonally). There is never more than one star in any square.

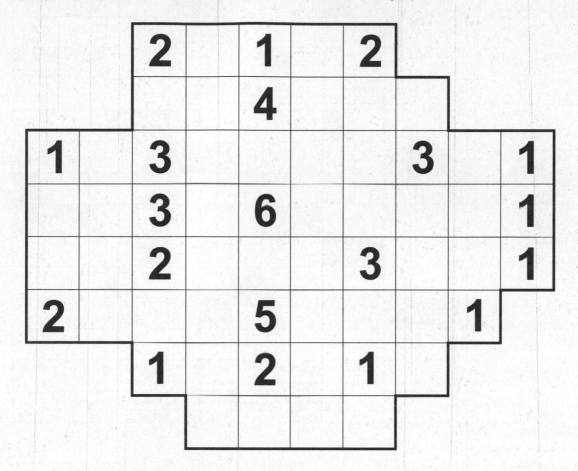

TELEPHONE TRIOS

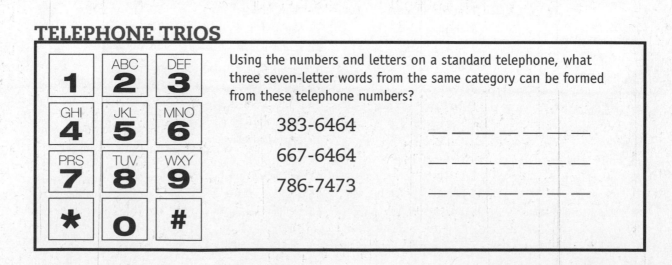

Using the numbers and letters on a standard telephone, what three seven-letter words from the same category can be formed from these telephone numbers?

383-6464 ＿ ＿ ＿ ＿ ＿ ＿ ＿

667-6464 ＿ ＿ ＿ ＿ ＿ ＿ ＿

786-7473 ＿ ＿ ＿ ＿ ＿ ＿ ＿

★★★★ Say What? by Merle Baker

ACROSS

1 "Take __ from me!"
5 Darts venues
9 Burst forth
14 Unexciting
15 Troop group
16 Stand for a chorus
17 Postal service
20 Tec
21 Set apart
22 Little bit
23 Lt. __
25 Hatshepsut, for one
29 __' Pea
31 Poisonous snake
33 Lion prey
34 One on the run
36 Museum or think follower
38 Baloney
42 Macbeth tormentor
43 Castle protectors
44 "__ Wiedersehen"
45 Lacks
47 Butter containers
51 Yet
54 Columbus Day mo.
56 After-tax amount
57 Soothes
59 Sukova of tennis
61 "Look who just came in!"
65 Mix up
66 River of Russia
67 Isthmus
68 Troop group
69 D-Day landers
70 Small bills

DOWN

1 White Sands events
2 CPA's expertise
3 Slow down
4 Place with llamas
5 Soft touch
6 Young'__
7 Bridge action
8 Treeless plain
9 All My Children role
10 Delaware or Missouri
11 Draw upon
12 A pop
13 Have a go at
18 List ender
19 Cowardly Lion portrayer
24 Claim on property
26 A long time
27 Some time back
28 Shade
30 Young newts
32 Senior dances
35 Tennis ump's call
36 Favorite
37 Part of M.I.T.
38 "No way!"
39 Soy product
40 It's inadvisable
41 Grips
42 Gangster's gun
45 Saintly radiance
46 Toddler, perhaps
48 Rough
49 Mom's admonishment
50 Corn holders
52 La __ Opera House
53 Not real
55 Senator Kennedy
58 Violins and violas: Abbr.
60 Late-night name
61 Airline to Oslo
62 Fictional composer Bach
63 End of an admissions office e-mail address
64 Stetson or sombrero

★★★ Straight Ahead

Enter the grid at one of the white squares at bottom, pass through all the blue squares, then leave the grid through another white square. You must travel horizontally or vertically in a straight line, and turn only to avoid passing through a black square.

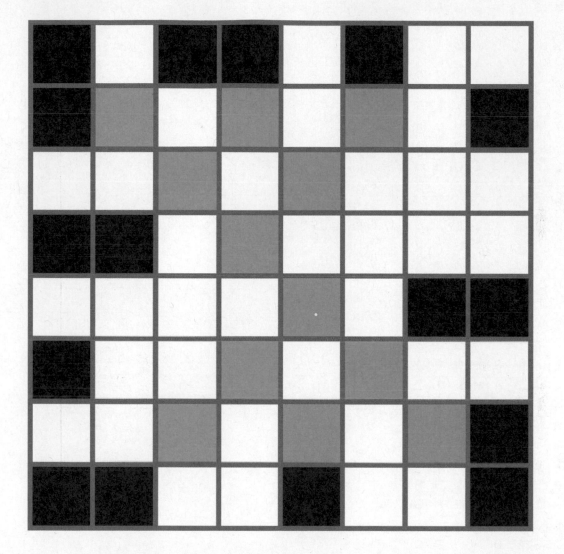

COMMON SENSE

What five-letter word can be found in the dictionary definitions of all of these words:

BIOSPHERE, CAKE, COBBLER, and VOLCANO?

— — — — —

★★ Biblical Spirals

The names of these Biblical characters are arranged in spiral shapes, either starting or finishing in the center, either clockwise or counterclockwise. Some of the spirals may overlap. One answer is shown to get you started.

```
T A L X D Q V Z H A D
A S L P S U A B E R A
N B A S R A L W Z E D
K T H H C H E R C O R
Q A M E Z R Y S U S N
H Y M L A H A D I L E
U S E T U S S S M M X
E A N F R E U N E L I
I A L E L I G Z C H M
A B L T H S J A E L E
R Z I E B A K T N B O
R E H J G F A B E A H
S U I D M L A B H W V
I D S A N T T H S T A
O N Y U S I B A R Z U
U C C H C O A S S I M
I H C E Y J B B A I D
X B A L R Q K S U I K
T I M E B P S E D R W
U S O E I B A M E T T
E H T X A H R C H T O
H C E H M M U O A L D
H A L S U T S U P P I
I M E P E E R A P O V
E B L A E N C H I N B
E I F P Y L A L E H G
U B A L Q U E R X Y C
J A R T G V D N A P O
A Z A H R Q N F W S K
```

ABIMELECH
AHASUERUS
AHIMELECH
ALEXANDER
ANTIOCHUS
ARCHELAUS
ARCHIPPUS
BALTHAZAR
BARSABBAS
BARZILLAI
BASHEMATH
BATHSHEBA
CORNELIUS
DEMETRIUS
DIONYSIUS
ELIMELECH
ELISABETH
EPAENETUS
HADADEZER
HAMMURABI
HYMENAEUS
LAPPIDOTH
SANBALLAT
~~TIMOTHEUS~~

TONGUE TWISTER

From what language are all of these words derived:

REPLICA, GRAFFITI, MEZZANINE, and CASINO?

A) Arabic B) Hindi C) Italian D) Greek

★★★ ABC

Enter the letters A, B, and C into the diagram so that each row and column has exactly one A, one B, and one C. The letters outside the diagram indicate the first letter encountered, moving in the direction of the arrow. Keep in mind that after all the letters have been filled in, there will be two blank boxes in each row and column.

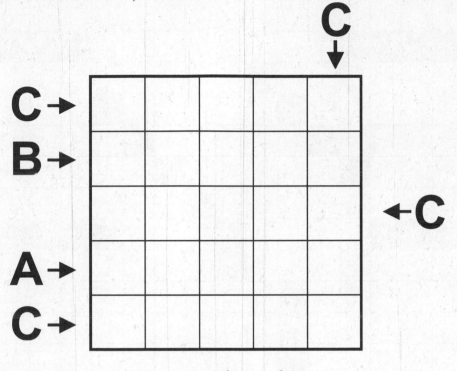

CLUELESS CROSSWORD

Complete the crossword with common uncapitalized seven-letter words, based entirely on the letters already filled in for you.

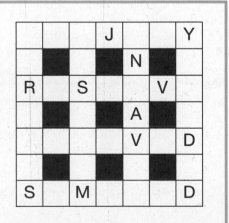

★★★★★ Themeless Toughie by Doug Peterson

ACROSS

1 Not paying attention
10 Cut of beef
15 Bombard with betas
16 Donne creation
17 In the sentencing phase
18 Get wider
19 Steady
20 Eyewash unit
22 HMO concern
23 Personal pronoun
24 Kind of clam
28 Nacre sources
32 Whip into shape
33 Court figures
34 Scrap
35 Ain't corrected
36 White's partner
37 Continental cabbage
38 Increase fraudulently
39 Become subject to
40 *Roots* actress
41 Reel from a belt
43 Opposite of blue
44 Little yapper
45 Sacramento paper
46 Glanced
49 Classroom need
54 Space Invaders maker
55 Reasons
57 Selena's surname
58 Soap Box Derby entry
59 Give body to
60 Rest areas

DOWN

1 Turns loose (on)
2 Stem
3 *Tom Thumb* composer
4 Knuckle under
5 Printing
6 Kitchen activity
7 *them* author
8 Western Indian
9 Elvis #1 tune
10 Stains
11 Gridiron star
12 Exceptionally
13 Dreaded figure
14 "Uh-uh!" in Ufa
21 Cooper, in *The Fountainhead*
24 Makeup accessories
25 Bears, to Brutus
26 Basic cable staple
27 Seriously affected
28 Menu phrase
29 "Forget it!"
30 Overthrow, perhaps
31 Lacking passion
33 Untouchable
36 Clog clearer
37 Check out
39 Complete Schedule A
40 Place for a cast
42 Allergens for some
43 Lipstick shade
45 Father
46 USMC rank
47 To ___ (precisely)
48 Uncommon, long ago
50 European auto
51 Major ending
52 Mouthpiece
53 Erstwhile political divs.
56 ___ roll

bRain BREaTHer
AIR TRAVEL ON THE CHEAP AND IN STYLE

Airports may well be the second circle of hell—but is being on the plane any better? Here are our favorite tips for making air travel as comfortable and economical as can be.

Know how to finagle frequent-flyer tickets and upgrades:

1. Book your free tickets *very* early. You have no excuse: Airline booking schedules are released a full 330 days in advance!

2. If you've been hearing that your airline of choice is headed toward bankruptcy, use up those miles quickly!

3. Call the airline directly if there's a specific flight for which you want to redeem your miles, even if their Web site says that that flight is blacked out. If the flight date is soon and the plane isn't booked, the airline may let you cash your miles in anyway.

Mix and match airports.
It's sometimes cheaper to take a return flight to a different airport than the one you flew out of, and it's an easy switch to make if you live in a big metropolitan area like New York, Chicago, or Washington D.C. For kicks, ask your travel agent or the airline customer service representative if this switcheroo can save you some money. (Of course, this trick only works if you're not parking your car at the airport.)

Don't settle for the first "bump" offer.
You're on an oversold flight, and the gate agents are starting to tempt passengers with flight coupons and the promise of an oversold flight. Never accept the agents' first offer—they have the discretion to give you even more money. Waiting patiently will be especially lucrative during holiday travel periods. Other fliers won't want to get bumped if Aunt Nellie will be at the destination airport, waiting for them.

Bump yourself preemptively.
If the waiting area looks packed and you're willing to bet the flight is oversold, go to the agents and offer up your seat before they start making their bump announcements. (You may even give them an opening bid of how much it would take in free vouchers for you to give up your spot.)

Get your problem resolved *after* takeoff.
Airline employees want you to have a pleasant flight not because they care about you, but because they don't want you to ruin everyone else's flight. If you have a bad seat, a noisy neighbor, or even a bad experience at the gate, talk to the chief purser, the person running all aspects of the flight (except, of course, flying the plane). Griping reasonably and rationally may get you a free drink, first-class food, or a first-class upgrade.

★★★★ Find the Ships

Determine the position of the 10 ships listed to the right of the diagram. The ships may be oriented either horizontally or vertically. A square with wavy lines indicates water and will not contain a ship. The numbers at the edge of the diagram indicate how many squares in that row or column contain parts of ships. When all 10 ships are correctly placed in the diagram, no two of them will touch each other, not even diagonally.

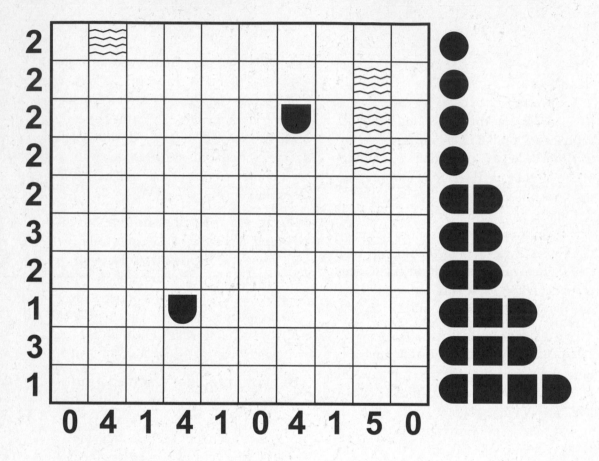

TWO-BY-FOUR

The eight letters in the word RENOWNED can be rearranged to form a pair of common four-letter words in three different ways, if no four-letter word is repeated. Can you find all three pairs of words?

___ ___ ___ ___ ___ ___ ___ ___ ___ ___ ___ ___

___ ___ ___ ___ ___ ___ ___ ___ ___ ___ ___ ___

★★★★ Hyper-Sudoku

Fill in the blank boxes so that every row, column, 3x3 box, *and* each of the four 3x3 gray regions contains all of the numbers 1 to 9.

			7		4			
5						7		
	4				6			
		1			5			2
8				9				
		4				1		
		3	6			8		
				4	3			
			8			2	7	

BETWEENER

What six-letter word belongs between the word at left and the word at right, so that the first and second word, and the second and third word, each form a common two-word phrase?

PAST _ _ _ _ _ _ PLAN

★★★★★ Themeless Toughie by S.N.

ACROSS

1 Striking
8 Go back
15 *Earth in the Balance* subject
16 Stable group
17 Harris' TV spouse
18 Light coats
19 Breaks up
20 Recreational vehicle
22 Symbol of confusion
23 FDR, circa 1912
26 Cites
30 Angle symbol, in trigonometry
32 Nonaggressive type
33 Took it
34 Heart
35 "Bringing Out the Best in Kids" club members
42 Some shoes
44 Cutoff
46 Grills
49 Shake
52 Shake
53 Heavy hammer
54 Out of control
56 Set down clearly
58 Fighting words
59 Like some outerwear
60 Roped in
61 They seldom blink

DOWN

1 Benefits
2 It may precede you
3 Developer's aides
4 Lame excuse of a sort
5 YWCA course
6 Germany/Poland border river
7 Most bronzed
8 Diamond, for example
9 Thought the same
10 Care
11 French ___
12 *Il Trovatore* role
13 Best New Artist Grammy recipient of 1961
14 "Happy Motoring!" wisher
21 Before
24 Stowe girl
25 Get on
27 Ready for letting
28 Hardly relaxed
29 Baby blues
30 Plane
31 Manta wearers
36 Arles adverb
37 Spanish hunter's cap
38 Even up
39 Looked down (at)
40 Denominate
41 Proclamation media
42 Tiniest bit
43 More like some soil
45 Tried to rend
47 Swiss mathematician
48 20 Across alternatives
49 Hosea follower
50 "Getting to Know You" singer
51 Modest beginning, so to speak
55 Grad students' jobs
57 Phi Beta's pride

★★★ Star Gathering

Enter the maze at top right, pass through all the stars, then exit. You must pass through the stars in this sequence: green, red, red, green, red, red, etc. You may not retrace your path.

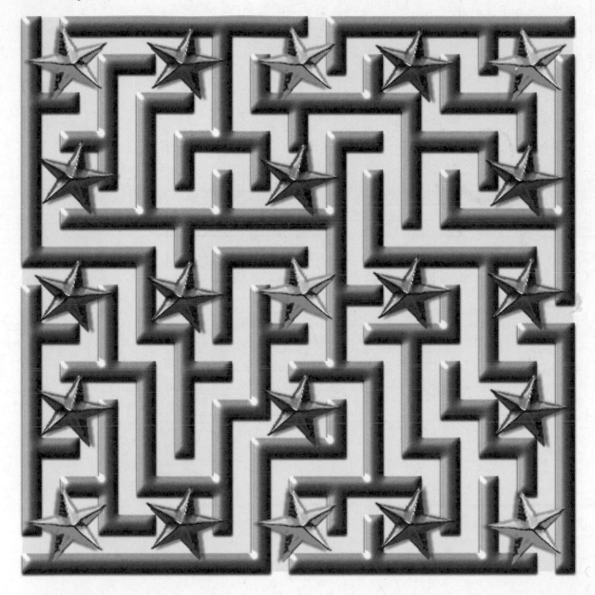

THREE AT A RHYME

Rearrange these letters to form three one-syllable words that rhyme.

C E E F L O R U U W Y

_____   _____   _____

★★★★ Circular Reasoning

Connect all of the circles by drawing a single continuous line through every square of the diagram. All right-angle turns of your line must alternate between boxes containing a circle and boxes not containing a circle. You must make a right-angle turn out of every square that contains a circle. Your line must end in the same square that it begins, and it cannot enter any square more than once.

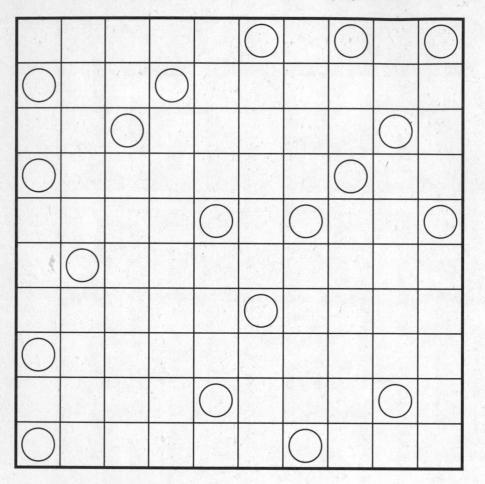

ADDITION SWITCH

Switch the positions of two of the digits in the incorrect sum at right, to get a correct sum.

```
  486
+ 273
-----
  660
```

★★★★★ Themeless Toughie by Daniel R. Stark

ACROSS

1 Stretched out
10 Put down
15 Molasses source
16 Sincerely
17 Good supply
18 *Law of the Lash* star
19 Usher
20 Sign
22 Element for Seurat
23 Aft opposite
24 Thirteen witches
27 World Series souvenirs
31 Gas
32 Shakespearean pronoun
33 Laugh syllable
34 Novelist Phillpotts
35 A long way
36 Ernie's roommate
37 Bungle
38 Hunters' wear
39 Trainer or bus
40 Kind of pancake batter
42 Pop singer Lauper
43 Etching fluid
44 High mountain
45 German cake
48 Holes in the ground
52 Cry of surprise
53 Too thin
56 Vast body
57 College student
58 Yonder ones
59 Diner freebie

DOWN

1 Parapsychology topic
2 Quiet time
3 Kind of molding
4 Mommy's mommy
5 Back or end
6 Doings
7 Gibe
8 Wrap up
9 Makes donuts
10 On the loose
11 Tonic
12 Subjective surroundings
13 Run words together
14 Gave the once-over
21 Fish-eating divers
24 Tight-knit team
25 Puccini genre
26 Manfred __ Richthofen
27 Summer flower
28 Out in front
29 *Danke*, in Dijon
30 Fourth man
31 Turn aside
32 Lack of confidence
35 Bess' successor
36 "__ appétit!"
38 Low-pressure system
39 Nicosia resident
41 NFL city
42 Bell-shaped hat
44 Yawning
45 Used up
46 Computer fixer
47 Lard alternative
49 Plucky
50 007 school
51 Bone-dry
54 Trim a fairway
55 Aachen article

★★★★ 123

Fill in the diagram so that each rectangular piece has one each of the numbers 1, 2, and 3, under these rules: 1) No two adjacent squares, horizontally or vertically, can have the same number. 2) Each completed row and column of the diagram will have an equal number of 1s, 2s, and 3s.

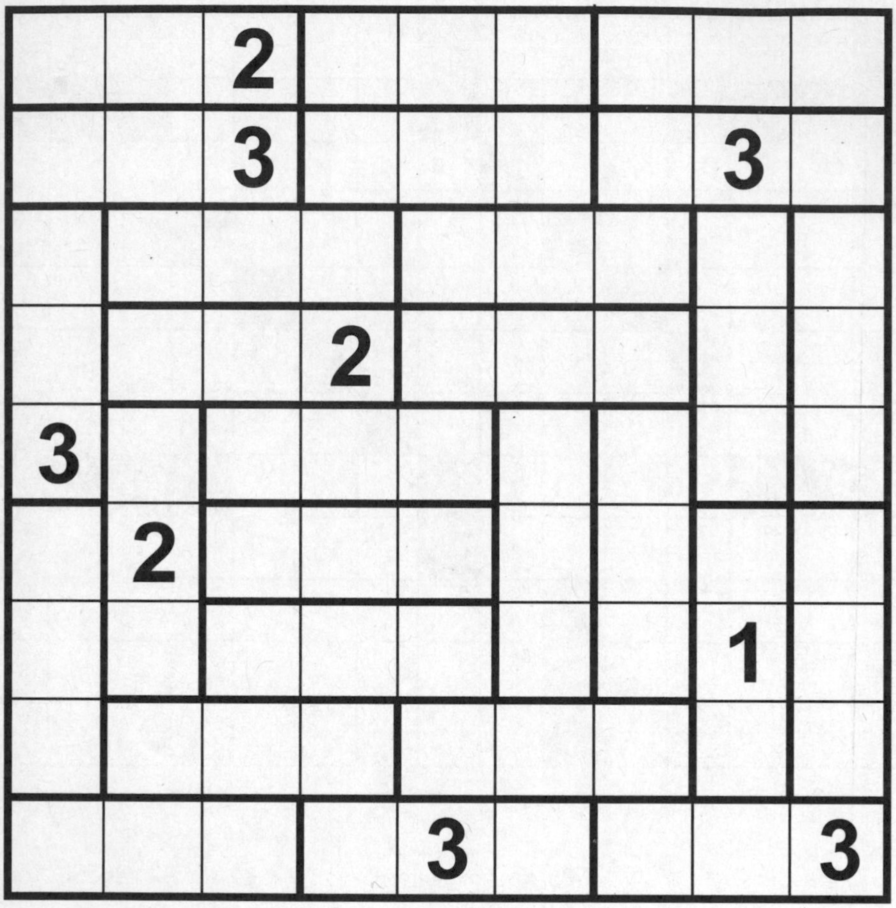

SUDOKU SUM

Without repeating any digits, complete the sum at right, by filling one digit in each of the five blanks.

$$
\begin{array}{r}
3\ \_\ 8 \\
+\ \_\ 5\ \_ \\
\hline
4\ \_\ \_
\end{array}
$$

★★★ Islands

Shade in some of the white squares in the diagram with "water," so that each remaining white box is part of an island. Each island will contain exactly one numbered square, indicating how many squares that island contains. Each island is separated from the other islands by water but may touch other islands diagonally. All water is connected, but there are no 2x2 regions of water in the diagram.

1						2	
		3					
					2		3
	4		2				
1		3					
					4		

AND SO ON

Unscramble the letters in the phrase CHASE OCEAN MIRE, to form two words that are part of a common phrase that has the word AND between them.

_____ and _____

★★★★★ Themeless Toughie by Doug Peterson

ACROSS

1 Balderdash

9 Postwar housing innovator

15 Sheer duds

16 Press agent?

17 *American Gothic* attire

18 Diacritical dot

19 Cartoonist Gardner

20 Holds

22 Demeter alias

23 Window alternative

25 Small vessel

27 Lexington's __ Arena

28 Originally

29 Hebrew prophet

31 "__ Good Turn Daily"

32 First name in Objectivism

34 His cardigan is in the Smithsonian

36 Some crustaceans

40 Apollo and Orpheus

41 CD player ancestor

43 *Full Metal Jacket* locale

44 Columnist LeShan

45 1972 Cooperstown inductee

47 Parisian pronoun

50 Half of a matching set

52 Court officials

53 Paganini's birthplace

55 Extra handle

57 Unpleasant residue

59 Fortune's start

60 Gourmet's love

62 Remote-control components

64 Less reasoned

65 1942 battle site

66 Professor, often

67 Showed dissatisfaction

DOWN

1 Uncultivated greenery

2 Like some help

3 Heebie-jeebies

4 Part of GM

5 Antietam general

6 Film director __ C. Kenton

7 '50s sitcom family

8 Respectful reply

9 Set off

10 Noted redhead

11 Slate examiner

12 Is unwelcome

13 Beam up

14 Cross the line, perhaps

21 Easter-egg design

24 Executed a Lutz

26 Thyroid neighbor

29 Type of paint

30 Circle dance

33 White Rose house

35 Childish demand

36 "Enough!"

37 Put out of action

38 Egg-shaped instruments

39 Turns about

42 Damon's pal

46 He coined the word "robotics"

48 Involve in intrigue

49 After-dark bash

51 Hagiography figure

53 Intimate

54 Syrian leader

56 Buccaneer's blade

58 Involve in intrigue

61 Boxer's warning

63 *What Not to Wear* network

★★★ "Z" as in "Puzzle"

25 seven-letter words, each containing one or more Z's, can be found in Z shapes in the diagram. One word is shown to get you started. Answers include four proper nouns and one hyphenated word.

```
H O R A B D I G I J B U Z K L Z M N N O
R I Z C A P G R O O F Z E Q R T D B A Z
Z O N P S T U C I T A R D S E I J O O Z
Y S T I Z E G T I Z T C A D Z G H O K A
G A Z K I M K Z E N H O T U R E T U Z U
H E P R A R I T Y S C H U V Z W B C G O
L L E Y O Z C W T Y E Z A B J A C Z O O
S B L M O N A N O R Z O P R R U S M A Z
T C E Z U V B E Z W A X Z B Z Z I C U D
E F A G H J J I L M S U B G O T Q R K A
R N N E Z A Q U E F O Z D J J E Z P R E
M A Z U B I Z H J K E R O P R E S T Z U
P R E H O A J K S Q U L N O B E L Z O O
R T A B R R E C D E F G D R I G H B A P
Z E L G R I Z Z E Z E E R Z Z L M O T C
T D L L O T R A Z X Y Y Z L E Q R I Z E
S G L A H O P K N P P S T G R I B U Z Z
T I Z G N E Z E O K I B P P Z D I F R E
B I E R Z O O M D F B C E Z L Y F G E H
H O R I S J H S D U T Z C E Z A A Z E R
```

IN OTHER WORDS

There is only one common uncapitalized word that contains the consecutive letters WNU. What's the word?

_____

★★★ Tattoo Maze

Connect each pair of identical tattoos with a separate path. No part of any path may be reused.

COMMON SENSE

What five-letter word can be found in the dictionary definitions of all of these words:

BRIDESMAID, GO-CART, NURSERY, and SQUIRT?

— — — — —

★★★★★ Themeless Toughie by Merle Baker

ACROSS

1 Funds
7 Arcade opening
15 Archeological site Tell el __
16 Fixed
17 Far from frivolous
18 Doesn't encourage
19 Like some limits
20 Insurance agt. designation
21 Composer Janácek
22 Conventions
25 Pottery product
28 South Carolina city
29 Pericardium, e.g.
32 Doesn't bounce
34 __ get-out
36 Upbraided
39 Take __ (stop)
40 Strategic positions
41 Tpks.
42 Depression
45 Combustible heap
46 Visibility aids
48 Famous reproach
51 Hollywood's st.
52 Touches up
56 Produce rapidly
58 And others
59 Orchestral offering
60 Retinue
61 Precipitate
62 Stirs

DOWN

1 Nest builder
2 Latin love
3 __ bonding
4 Bread spread
5 Not fulfilled
6 Part of a logarithm
7 Drake, for one
8 Diner order
9 Lay
10 Scand. land
11 Lifted
12 Of current interest
13 Bread spread
14 1994 Shirley MacLaine title role
23 Drop out
24 Quality
25 *Dreams of Gerontius* composer
26 Not everyday
27 Ranch feature
29 Not tight
30 Remodel
31 Wind up
33 Between, overseas
35 Recovers
37 *M* director
38 Fordable, perhaps
43 Supply
44 Architectural spiral
46 Cap wearer
47 Joe Buck's friend
48 Behold: Lat.
49 High-tech suffix
50 Distinctive quality
53 Sour fruit
54 Lighthearted
55 Makes doilies
57 Understanding

★★★★ ABCD

Enter the letters A, B, C, and D into the diagram so that each row and column has exactly one A, one B, one C, and one D. The letters outside the diagram indicate the first letter encountered, moving in the direction of the arrow. Keep in mind that after all the letters have been filled in, there will be two blank boxes in each row and column.

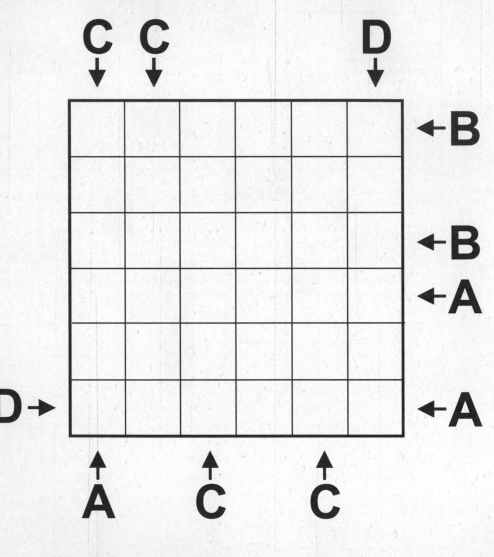

CITY SEARCH

Using the letters in EDINBURGH, we were able to form only one common uncapitalized seven-letter word. Can you find it?

_ _ _ _ _ _ _

★★★★ Sudoku

Fill in the blank boxes so that every row, column, and 3x3 box contains all of the numbers 1 to 9.

8		5	2			9		
				4				
4				3	8			5
					5			
		3				7		8
	5	2		6				9
	3					6		
				1			4	
2		9						

MIXAGRAMS

Each line contains a five-letter word and a four-letter word that have been mixed together (the order of the letters in each word has not been changed). Unmix the two words on each line and write them in the spaces provided. When you're done, find a two-part answer to the clue by reading down the letter columns in the answers.

CLUE: Baloney

C O M O C I O T A = _ _ _ _ _ + _ _ _ _

B L A P O S A R E = _ _ _ _ _ + _ _ _ _

T A N G U B E A R = _ _ _ _ _ + _ _ _ _

C A P O R S I P T = _ _ _ _ _ + _ _ _ _

★★★★★ Themeless Toughie by Daniel R. Stark

ACROSS

1 Bearlike beasts
7 Was restless
15 Seeing red?
16 Asia's __ Mountains
17 Business book
18 Boss
19 Unseal, to Blake
20 Undue pressure
22 Wholesale quantity
23 Processes cotton
25 Jane ex
26 Ward off
27 Started over
29 *Sweet Dreams* subject
32 Farm structure
33 Very sharp
34 Church holdings
36 Something to keep
38 Recipe word
42 Sawlike chain
44 Less common
45 Bitter __
48 Studio feature
49 Threnody
50 Staggers around
52 Jellyfish habitat
54 Khartoum's river
55 Movie dog
56 Mideast port
59 Pewter part
60 Normal
62 Maraud
64 OK to participate
65 Rights a wrong
66 Let go
67 Ice hockey team

DOWN

1 More than two
pounds

2 Integrated
3 Codicil
4 Trip part
5 Not up
6 Put on airs
7 Coax
8 Crater edges
9 Sources of trouble
10 Pump qty.
11 *Daily Planet* logo
12 Easy baskets
13 Hole in your shoe

14 In a sinister manner
21 Clergy members
24 Some are historic
26 Slow down
28 Refuses to grant
30 Breathing aid
31 Society column word
35 Goya's homeland
37 Bags at the market
39 Pest
40 Kind of robe
41 Least experienced

43 Had an address
45 Classroom missile
46 Get cozy
47 Fine print
51 *Tootsie* Oscar winner
53 What psychics
may see
56 *Tiny Toons* bunny
57 Dashiell's peer
58 London art gallery
61 A day in 35 Down
63 Voice: Lat.

★★★★ One-Way Streets

The diagram represents a pattern of streets. Ps are parking spaces, and the black squares are stores. Find the route that starts at a parking space, passes through all stores exactly once, and ends at the other parking space. Arrows indicate one-way traffic for that block only. No block or intersection may be entered more than once.

SOUND THINKING

We can think of two common uncapitalized words whose only consonant sounds are M, B, and S, in that order. How many can you think of?

_____　_____

★★★ Split Decisions

In this clueless crossword puzzle, each answer consists of two words whose spellings are the same, except for the consecutive letters given. All answers are common words; no phrases or hyphenated or capitalized words are used. Some of the clues may have more than one solution, but there is only one word pair that will correctly link up with all the other word pairs.

TRANSDELETION

Delete one letter from the word PELICANS and rearrange the rest, to get a two-word photography term.

_____ _____

★★★★★ Themeless Toughie by S.N.

ACROSS

1 They look ahead
12 Loses badly
14 Sports story of '75
16 Press
17 Catch
18 Places with pools
19 Steals, slangily
22 Principles
24 Fay, in *King Kong*
25 Outback dweller
29 Corroded
30 Go with
31 Home buyer's concern
32 Tally, with "up"
33 Night __
34 Validates
37 Astronomical observation
39 Mime's moniker
42 *Ah, Wilderness!* character
43 '30s poster style
44 Compass reading
45 Builds
47 Gets moving
49 View from *A Room With a View*
50 *Ash Wednesday* monogram
53 "I agree!"
54 They're enshrined in Baltimore
59 One from Freetown
60 Strike caller

DOWN

1 Remote
2 Tom, Noah and Ruthie, e.g.
3 Th.D. curriculum
4 Night-sch. course
5 Billy Rose in *Funny Lady*
6 Rosemary Murphy's hubby
7 Propelled
8 Pompom locale
9 H
10 Hair conditioner
11 Criticize
12 Angelic rank
13 Affirmative response
14 Oktoberfest needs
15 Stocks or bonds
20 Cartoon Network sister station
21 Supports
22 Linus Pauling alma mater
23 White-hat wearers
26 "Go ahead!"
27 Pester
28 *Gallery of the Louvre* painter
34 NBA MVP in 2000
35 *Even Big Guys Cry* author
36 Letter-writing guide
37 Entangle
38 In the bargain
39 Soil
40 Confine
41 Untrained hands
46 Miles Davis colleague
48 Beneficiary
50 Peter or Paul
51 Win over
52 Olympic sport
55 "The Moon, how definite its __!": Coleridge
56 Least expensive ticket
57 Mauna __
58 Further

★★★★ Looped Path

Draw a continuous, unbroken loop that passes through each of the red, blue, and white squares exactly once. Move from square to square in a straight line or by turning left or right, but never diagonally. You must alternate passing through red and blue squares, with any number of white squares in between.

COMMON SENSE

What six-letter word can be found in the dictionary definitions of all of these words:

CLOSING COSTS, FRISK, PARTY, and QUARRY?

_ _ _ _ _ _

★★★★ Star Search

Find the stars that are hidden in some of the blank squares. The numbered squares indicate how many stars are hidden in the squares adjacent to them (including diagonally). There is never more than one star in any square.

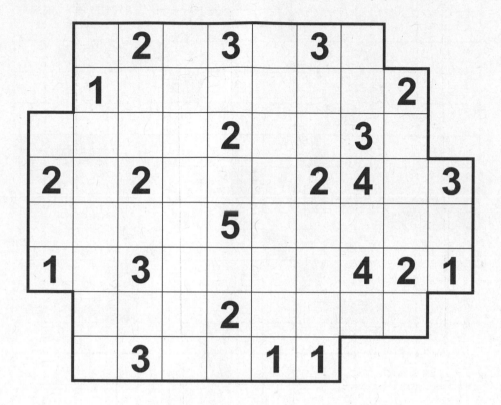

TELEPHONE TRIOS

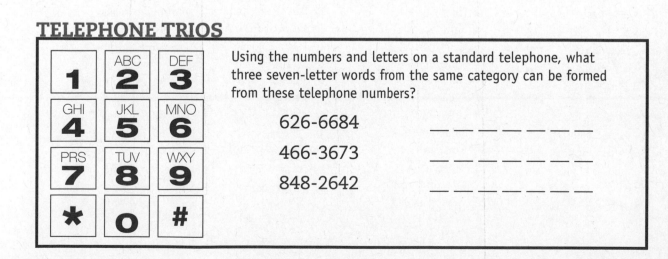

Using the numbers and letters on a standard telephone, what three seven-letter words from the same category can be formed from these telephone numbers?

626-6684　　_ _ _ _ _ _ _

466-3673　　_ _ _ _ _ _ _

848-2642　　_ _ _ _ _ _ _

★★★★★ **Themeless Toughie** by Daniel R. Stark

ACROSS

1 Sadie Hawkins creator
7 Takes back
15 Large quantity
16 Clyde Cessna's field
17 Sonata movements
18 Feud
19 Rubber-stamps
20 Draw off
22 Account exec
23 See the point of
24 Antler bearers
25 Like good raisins
27 Haik wearer
29 Lemon drink
30 Over-refined
31 Fit
33 Attempts
35 Ask earnestly
37 Threads
41 Tuition recipient
43 The former Mrs. Ryan Phillippe
44 Result
47 Shared a border
49 Floppy contents
50 Moto portrayer
51 Wind-borne silt
53 Flower covering
54 Ivy in *Batman & Robin*
55 '80s Best Picture
56 Shelter
57 Meaning
60 Eventually
62 Diplomatic compounds
63 Curbed
64 Most expensive
65 Harris and Irish

DOWN

1 Rescind
2 Spectator
3 Fixed
4 Build on
5 Walks heavily
6 Former Spanish money
7 Wreaks havoc on
8 Levels off
9 Salon bottle
10 Wonderful
11 Wolfed down
12 Vitamin C source
13 Tribal emblems
14 Quick
21 West Point group
25 He played the Wiz
26 In the phone book
28 Sahara nomad
30 Intimate
32 Die face
34 Diatribe
36 __ form
38 Article preceder
39 Admired greatly
40 Anagram of "seesawed"
42 In between
44 Slips past
45 Stir up
46 Where *six* means "six"
48 Jeans partner
51 Byways
52 Tendon
55 Move some
58 "... 'Round the __ Oak Tree"
59 Select
61 Dressy accessory

★★★★ Islands

Shade in some of the white squares in the diagram with "water," so that each remaining white box is part of an island. Each island will contain exactly one numbered square, indicating how many squares that island contains. Each island is separated from the other islands by water but may touch other islands diagonally. All water is connected, but there are no 2x2 regions of water in the diagram.

		4				3			
				3					1
4			1						
					3				2
3									
			3			3			
2								1	
			6						
	5								

AND SO ON

Unscramble the letters in the phrase MEAGER SUSHI STEW, to form two words that are part of a common phrase that has the word AND between them.

_____ and _____

★★★★ Line Drawing

Draw four straight lines, each from one edge of the square to another edge, so that the same six letters appear in each of the five regions. Then form five different words from each group of six letters.

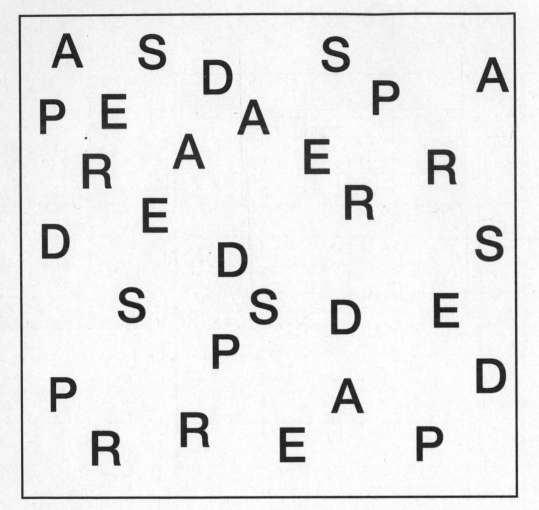

TWO-BY-FOUR

The eight letters in the word MOVEMENT can be rearranged to form a pair of common four-letter words in only one way. Can you find the two words?

__ __ __ __   __ __ __ __

★★★★★ Themeless Toughie by Merle Baker

ACROSS

1 Secure
5 Scottish landowner
10 Cookery paste
14 Canadian pop singer
15 Precise
17 Genesis name
18 Seeing that
19 Designer Schiaparelli
20 Some marsupials
21 Crowd sound
22 Small particle: Abbr.
23 Vital
24 It "favors the prepared mind"
25 Spot near the Acropolis
27 Composer Janácek
29 Article written by Freud
30 Brando had it
34 Be mindful of
38 Track equipment
39 S.A. country
42 Cubic Rubik
43 Long lunches
44 Guinea-pig relative
46 Bldg. unit
48 Panhandle setting: Abbr.
49 "See ya!"
50 *Blondie* character
52 Flaky mineral
53 Overboard
55 Gibson, in *Braveheart*
56 Conceived of
57 Look impressed
58 Spotted
59 It's rarely a hit
60 Tireless runner

DOWN

1 Diving gear
2 Parallel
3 Downhill place
4 River of Kenya
5 French wine valley
6 Hector
7 "Make __" (Picard's command)
8 Greek letters
9 Brooklynese article
10 Café order
11 Under control
12 Medium setting
13 Shade of white
16 In demand
23 Skilled choppers
24 RNA triplet
26 Cong. members
27 Blame on
28 "... __ saw Elba"
31 Complicate
32 Forked-tailed flier
33 Homeowner's pymt.
35 Slapstick
36 Doctor's instrument
37 Paraphrased
39 Layered minerals
40 Fixed
41 Shed tears
45 Restrict
46 Thin as __
47 How a French dance begins?
50 Bus. leaders
51 Directional starter
52 E-mail
54 Vault supporter

★★ Triad Split Decisions

In this clueless crossword puzzle, each answer consists of two words whose spellings are the same, except for the consecutive letters given. All answers are common words; no phrases or hyphenated or capitalized words are used. Some of the clues may have more than one solution, but there is only one word pair that will correctly link up with all the other word pairs.

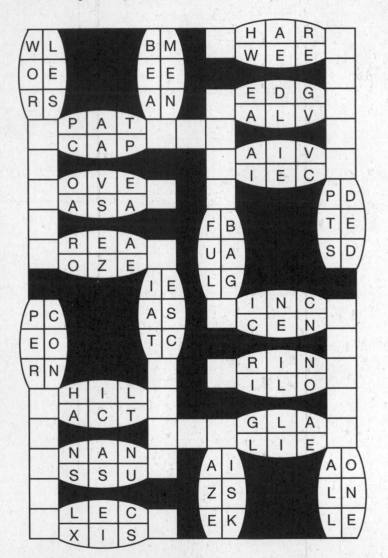

TRANSDELETION

Delete one letter from the word LEVITATOR and rearrange the rest, to get the name of a famous philosopher. Then delete one letter from the word LEVITATORS and rearrange the rest, to get the name of another famous philosopher.

_____   _____

★★★★ Castle Tour

Entering and exiting as the arrows indicate, find the longest way through the maze without retracing your path. You may go over and under the bridge at the center.

THREE AT A RHYME

Rearrange these letters to form three one-syllable words that rhyme.

A C E E F I I I R R R R T

_____   _____   _____

★★★★★ Themeless Toughie Daniel R. Stark

ACROSS

1 Treat harshly
8 Low country
15 Tiara
16 Queen of Henry II
17 Gas or water
18 Notwithstanding
19 Reveled in
20 City on the Bight of Benin
22 Kettle and Bell
23 Latin 101 verb
24 Dwells
25 Pats on
26 Habitué, as at the mall
27 One might be early
28 Boxer's quest
29 Building material
31 Polls
33 Batter's need
34 Profile, briefly
35 Doesn't quite say
39 Tamper with
42 Must-haves
43 Kind of canoe
45 Caesar's man
47 Cookie holders
48 Dispirit
49 *Algiers* character
50 Hairpin curve
51 Alaskan city
52 Change at de Gaulle Airport
53 Literally, "kitchen"
55 From Valletta
57 Fitness guru
58 Be derivative
59 Wire sources
60 Used no power

DOWN

1 Telescope lens
2 View from the FDR Memorial
3 Personal
4 Cameos, maybe
5 Tennyson heroine
6 Firm up
7 Beauty consultant
8 Fence-sitters
9 Some spreads
10 Below, with "than"
11 Quarter-mile, at times
12 Cheer up
13 In particular
14 Prepares to perform
21 Summer cooler
24 Blast
25 Piece of turf
27 Kelly's cohort
28 One of 13 in bridge
30 Puts together
32 *Das Boot* craft
35 Vaccinates
36 Use a ruler
37 Popular pet
38 Goalies and wings
39 Forceful
40 Emulate Falstaff
41 Witty retort
44 Puffin relative
46 Fix the lawn
48 Eatery, or its patron
49 Green taps
51 Calculator button
52 "A Chapter on Ears" essayist
54 Tom Sawyer's half-brother
56 Boss, in Barcelona

PAGE 17
Take the Cake

L	I	F	E		R	E	D	S		P	A	S	T	A
O	R	E	O		E	L	I	A		R	A	P	I	D
P	O	U	N	D	S	I	G	N		E	R	O	D	E
E	N	D		R	O	O	S	T		C	O	N	E	S
			S	O	R	T		I	C	I	N	G		
	S	C	E	N	T		T	A	O	S		E	P	A
S	H	O	R	E		O	G	R	E		B	A	M	
T	I	F	F		B	A	T	O	N		D	A	R	E
A	R	F		S	A	S	E		C	U	T	I	N	
R	T	E		P	A	S	S		B	L	A	H	S	
	E	R	A	S	E		R	A	I	L				
P	O	S	E	R		S	T	E	R	N		S	T	S
U	S	H	E	R		S	H	O	R	T	S	T	O	P
T	H	O	S	E		E	R	I	E		P	E	R	U
T	A	P	E	D		D	U	L	L		A	W	E	D

PAGE 18
Bar Tending

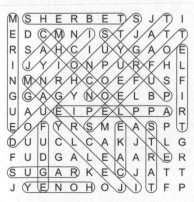

COUNTDOWN
9-8+76-54+3-21 = 5

PAGE 19
Sweet Stuff

INITIAL REACTION
32 = OUNCES in a QUART

PAGE 20
Sudoku

2	8	9	6	4	7	5	3	1
6	4	1	8	3	5	2	9	7
7	3	5	1	9	2	4	8	6
4	6	3	5	2	9	1	7	8
9	5	7	4	1	8	6	2	3
1	2	8	7	6	3	9	4	5
5	9	2	3	7	1	8	6	4
3	1	4	9	8	6	7	5	2
8	7	6	2	5	4	3	1	9

MIXAGRAMS

CAMEL   RICE
HEATH   COAL
SPIEL   CALM
BILGE   FOLD

PAGE 21
On Foot

S	A	D	A	T		P	O	E	M		S	P	A	R
I	N	U	S	E		A	L	V	A		A	R	C	H
S	T	E	P	L	A	D	D	E	R		L	I	L	O
	S	T	I	L	L	S		A	B	A	C	U	S	
			C	E	O		A	R	C	A	D	E		
P	E	W		R	E	T	R	E	A	D		H	A	T
A	L	I	A	S		O	T	I	S		R	I	D	E
T	O	N	Y		R	I	G		A	K	I	N		
S	P	I	N		A	S	S	N		S	T	E	E	P
Y	E	N		T	R	O	I	S	K	Y		S	U	M
		A	T	E	A	S	E		I	S	A			
P	O	W	E	L	L		E	N	T	R	E	E		
I	R	A	N		S	T	R	I	D	E	N	T	L	Y
E	L	L	S		E	R	I	N		M	I	A	M	I
T	Y	K	E		A	I	D	E		S	E	T	O	N

PAGE 22
Circular Reasoning

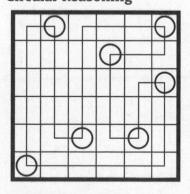

ADDITION SWITCH
820 + 147 = 967

PAGE 23
Line Drawing

ONE, TWO, THREE, NINE, TWELVE, SEVENTEEN

THREE OF A KIND
WE DO <u>HOPE</u> SOME <u>ST</u>ORES WILL HAVE A SALE ON <u>KIT</u>CHENWARE.

PAGE 24
Security Checks

C K E E P O U Q D J V D
H R M O E S H U T O U O
A D T Y D E V I C E G I
I S E P A D L O C K S S
N T E R C E S E C R T T
S O F V I S H U T O U T
R U G T R W M T Z O F G
B E O C R R D S P E A E
D E D C A K F E N C R R
D R A L B S E C B I A A
A O A C I K E U X R L W
U R G U O G W R C E A E
G O H L G N H I R L R B
Y R T N E O N T P A B E
S K C E H O S Y C C T N

TONGUE TWISTER
FRENCH

PAGE 25
City Structures

S	T	A	R		S	T	O	P		S	H	A	P	E
C	U	B	A		T	A	M	E		N	O	S	E	Y
A	L	O	T		A	R	E	A		A	M	P	L	E
R	I	V	E	R	B	A	N	K		P	E	S	T	S
		P	E	D	A	L		S	L	A	P			
			R	E	N	T		A	T	L	A	S		
S	P	A	C	E		O	O	P	S		A	L	T	O
A	R	C	H		A	N	D	E	S		T	O	U	R
P	E	R	U		S	O	A	R		T	E	E	N	S
		P	E	R	C	H		Y	M	C	A			
			C	H	E	F		A	L	O	F	T		
C	A	C	H	E		O	L	D	S	C	H	O	O	L
E	V	O	K	E		R	I	O	T		A	C	T	I
N	E	V	E	R		C	A	L	L		R	U	E	S
T	R	E	Y	S		E	R	L	E		A	S	S	T

PAGE 26
Islands

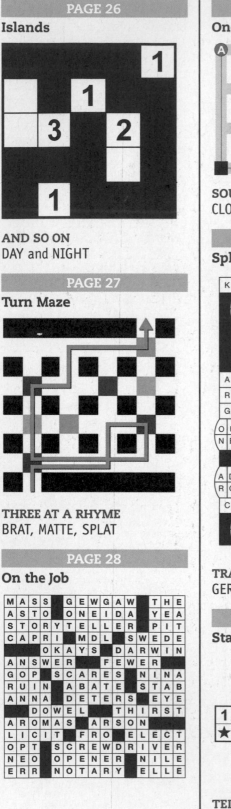

AND SO ON
DAY and NIGHT

PAGE 27
Turn Maze

THREE AT A RHYME
BRAT, MATTE, SPLAT

PAGE 28
On the Job

PAGE 29
One-Way Streets

SOUND THINKING
CLOG, COLLEAGUE

PAGE 30
Split Decisions

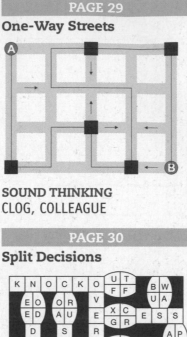

TRANSDELETION
GERANIUM

PAGE 31
Star Search

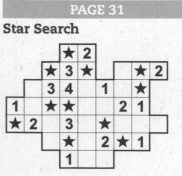

TELEPHONE TRIOS
MACBETH, SHYLOCK, OTHELLO

PAGE 32
Deep Thinking

IN OTHER WORDS
EASYGOING

PAGE 33
Simple Puzzle

A	B	B	R		M	O	D	E	S		S	A	N	K
M	E	R	E		T	U	R	N	A		C	H	I	N
E	L	E	M	E	N	T	A	R	Y		R	A	N	I
N	A	D	I	A		S	T	A	S		A	B	E	T
			T	R	A	P		G	N	A	T			
A	C	T		P	I	E	C	E	O	F	C	A	K	E
N	E	R	O		M	N	O		T	H	R	E	E	
N	L	E	R	S		T	A	S		S	E	G	A	L
A	L	A	C	K			S	H	H		D	O	N	E
N	O	T	H	I	N	G	T	O	I	T		N	E	D
		E	M	I	R		V	E	I	L				
F	I	B	S		E	A	V	E		E	A	G	L	E
E	D	I	T		C	H	I	L	D	S	P	L	A	Y
R	E	A	R		E	A	S	E	D		S	O	M	E
N	A	S	A		S	M	A	R	T		E	W	E	S

PAGE 34
Hyper-Sudoku

3	8	1	4	5	9	6	7	2
7	5	9	6	2	3	4	1	8
6	4	2	8	1	7	5	9	3
9	1	7	3	4	6	8	2	5
8	6	5	2	7	1	3	4	9
2	3	4	5	9	8	1	6	7
4	7	8	1	3	2	9	5	6
5	2	6	9	8	4	7	3	1
1	9	3	7	6	5	2	8	4

MIXAGRAMS

C R E S S H U L K
U P P E D F O I L
F L A R E O I N K
F L U T E O A K S

PAGE 35

Flower Power

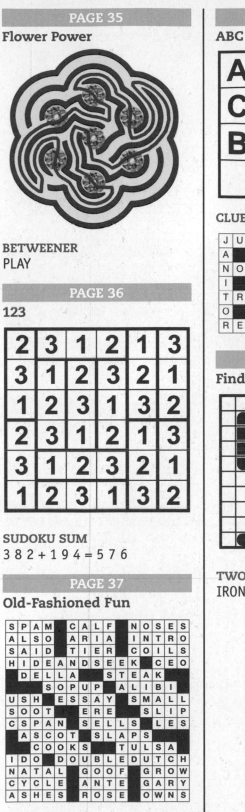

BETWEENER
PLAY

PAGE 36

123

2	3	1	2	1	3
3	1	2	3	2	1
1	2	3	1	3	2
2	3	1	2	1	3
3	1	2	3	2	1
1	2	3	1	3	2

SUDOKU SUM
3 8 2 + 1 9 4 = 5 7 6

PAGE 37

Old-Fashioned Fun

S	P	A	M		C	A	L	F		N	O	S	E	S
A	L	S	O		A	R	I	A		I	N	T	R	O
S	A	I	D		T	I	E	R		C	O	I	L	S
H	I	D	E	A	N	D	S	E	E	K		C	E	O
	D	E	L	L	A			S	T	E	A	K		
		S	O	P	U	P		A	L	I	B	I		
U	S	H		E	S	S	A	Y		S	M	A	L	L
S	O	O	T			E	R	E			S	L	I	P
C	S	P	A	N		S	E	L	L	S		L	E	S
	A	S	C	O	T		S	L	A	P	S			
		C	O	O	K	S			T	U	L	S	A	
I	D	O		D	O	U	B	L	E	D	U	T	C	H
N	A	T	A	L		G	O	O	F		G	R	O	W
C	Y	C	L	E		A	N	T	E		G	A	R	Y
A	S	H	E	S		R	O	S	E		O	W	N	S

PAGE 38

ABC

A		B	C
C	A		B
B	C	A	
	B	C	A

CLUELESS CROSSWORD

J	U	G	U	L	A	R
A		E		A		U
N	O	T	I	C	E	D
I		T		Q		D
T	R	I	B	U	T	E
O		N		E		R
R	E	G	A	R	D	S

PAGE 39

Find the Ships

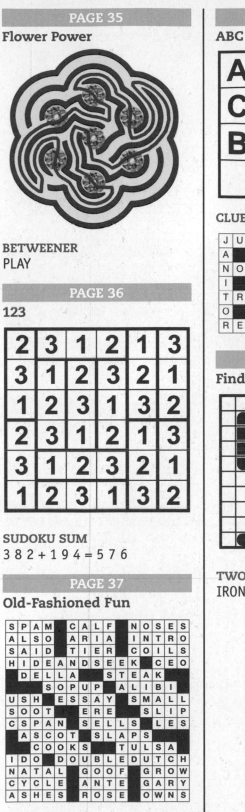

TWO-BY-FOUR
IRON, YARD

PAGE 40

No Go

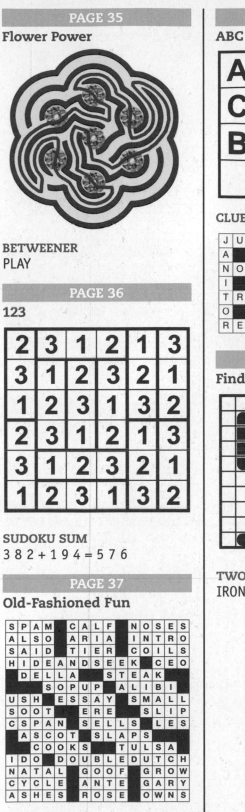

INITIAL REACTION
12 = BUTTONS on a TELEPHONE
(including the ASTERISK and
POUND SIGN)

PAGE 41

Up in the Air

W	A	S	P		L	O	L	A		S	L	A	S	H
A	N	N	A		O	R	E	S		L	O	T	T	O
S	T	A	T		G	N	A	T		E	A	T	I	N
H	I	G	H	A	S	A	K	I	T	E		I	N	K
		S	W	I	M	S		E	V	I	C	T	S	
P	A	T		O	N	E		G	L	E	N			
F	L	A	S	K		N	E	I	L		A	S	K	S
C	A	R	P	E	N	T	E	R	S	P	L	A	N	E
S	I	S	I		Y	E	L	L		A	L	I	E	N
		C	O	L	D		S	A	G		L	E	D	
C	O	M	E	T	O		A	C	M	E	S			
I	C	E		O	N	C	L	O	U	D	N	I	N	E
R	E	T	R	O		L	O	U	S		A	R	E	A
C	A	R	O	L		A	N	T	E		C	A	R	S
A	N	O	D	E		M	E	S	S		K	N	O	T

PAGE 42

Ring Links

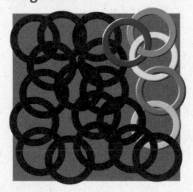

THREE AT A RHYME
FOE, TOW, WHOA

PAGE 43

Circular Reasoning

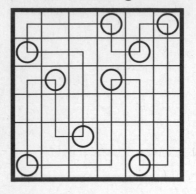

ADDITION SWITCH
2 6 6 + 3 7 5 = 6 4 1

PAGE 44

Let's Eat Out

B	S	I	L	E	R	F	C	G	S	S	P
R	R	B	J	T	R	H	H	R	G	R	U
E	E	S	O	I	D	S	A	A	T	E	H
F	M	T	E	O	I	U	L	T	U	G	C
I	O	S	S	L	T	A	K	U	O	R	T
L	T	S	E	I	F	H	B	I	O	U	E
L	S	R	O	S	G	F	O	T	H	B	K
S	U	F	B	D	E	E	A	Y	K	M	T
D	C	I	A	T	A	N	R	W	Y	A	R
Y	R	E	L	T	U	C	D	H	X	H	I
M	I	L	K	S	H	A	K	E	S	T	B
T	O	L	G	N	I	K	R	A	P	A	W
T	O	P	E	E	F	F	O	C	C	S	C
W	A	I	T	R	E	S	S	Q	I	R	F
B	O	O	T	Z	J	U	K	E	B	O	X

TONGUE TWISTER
SANSKRIT

PAGE 45

Cornered

N	A	V	A	L		A	W	E	D		E	C	H	O
A	L	I	B	I		L	I	A	R		L	U	A	U
B	L	O	C	K	P	A	R	T	Y		O	B	I	T
O	I	L		E	A	S	E		W	I	P	E	R	S
B	E	A	T	N	I	K		S	A	T	E	S		
			R	E	D	A	P	P	L	E		T	O	W
E	L	B	O	W		H	E	L	M		E	G	O	
L	O	O	T			B	O	W			D	A	R	E
S	I	X		S	C	A	T			D	U	K	E	S
E	S	S		C	A	B	O	O	S	E	S			
			P	L	A	N	E		C	O	S	T	A	R	S
M	A	R	I	N	A		B	T	U	S		M	O	O
E	R	I	N		S	Q	U	A	R	E	D	E	A	L
S	I	N	K		T	U	R	N		R	I	N	S	E
S	A	G	S		A	O	N	E		T	E	S	T	S

PAGE 46

Sudoku

6	3	2	8	4	1	9	5	7
7	9	8	6	5	3	4	1	2
4	5	1	9	7	2	8	6	3
1	4	3	2	6	8	7	9	5
8	6	7	5	1	9	2	3	4
5	2	9	7	3	4	1	8	6
2	7	5	1	8	6	3	4	9
3	1	6	4	9	7	5	2	8
9	8	4	3	2	5	6	7	1

MIXAGRAMS

A	L	L	O	W		Y	O	G	A
J	U	N	T	A		I	D	L	Y
R	A	D	A	R		P	L	O	P
P	R	I	S	M		K	I	W	I

PAGE 47

123

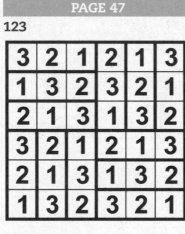

3	2	1	2	1	3
1	3	2	3	2	1
2	1	3	1	3	2
3	2	1	2	1	3
2	1	3	1	3	2
1	3	2	3	2	1

SUDOKU SUM
2 7 5 + 1 0 9 = 3 8 4

PAGE 48

Watch It

J	E	S	T		A	M	E	S		C	A	C	H	E
E	X	P	O		M	O	L	E		O	L	L	I	E
S	P	O	T		I	S	L	E		B	L	A	D	E
S	E	C	O	N	D	H	A	N	D	R	O	S	E	
E	L	K		E	S	E			R	A	T	S		
			P	S	T		F	B	I		S	I	T	E
L	O	B	E	S		O	L	I	V	E		C	A	W
S	H	O	W	I	N	G	O	N	E	S	F	A	C	E
A	I	S		E	U	R	O	S		C	O	L	T	S
T	O	S	S		R	E	D		O	R	E			
	A	I	R	S			A	D	O		A	D	S	
O	N	T	H	E	B	A	N	D	W	A	G	O	N	
P	H	O	T	O		L	I	N	E		T	I	D	E
R	O	V	E	D		O	D	E	S		O	L	G	A
O	H	A	R	E		T	E	X	T		P	E	E	K

PAGE 49

One-Way Streets

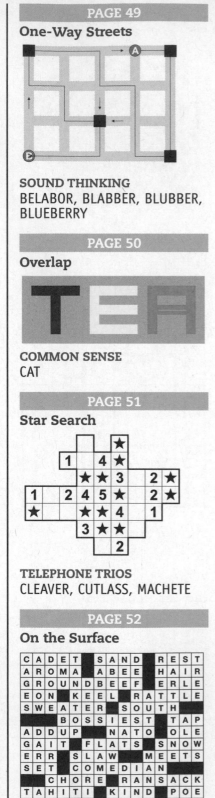

SOUND THINKING
BELABOR, BLABBER, BLUBBER, BLUEBERRY

PAGE 50

Overlap

TEA

COMMON SENSE
CAT

PAGE 51

Star Search

					★
	1		4	★	
		★	★	3		2	★
1		2	4	5	★		2	★
★			★	★	4		1
	3	★	★		
		2			

TELEPHONE TRIOS
CLEAVER, CUTLASS, MACHETE

PAGE 52

On the Surface

C	A	D	E	T		S	A	N	D		R	E	S	T
A	R	O	M	A		A	B	E	E		H	A	I	R
G	R	O	U	N	D	B	E	E	F		E	R	L	E
E	O	N		K	E	E	L		R	A	T	T	L	E
S	W	E	A	T	E	R		S	O	U	T	H		
			B	O	S	S	I	E	S	T		T	A	P
A	D	D	U	P		N	A	T	O		O	L	E	
G	A	I	T		F	L	A	T	S		S	N	O	W
E	R	R		S	L	A	W		M	E	E	T	S	
S	E	T		C	O	M	E	D	I	A	N			
			C	H	O	R	E		R	A	N	S	A	C	K
T	A	H	I	T	I		K	I	N	D		P	O	E
A	X	E	L		S	O	I	L	S	A	M	P	L	E
R	E	A	L		T	A	L	L		T	U	L	I	P
A	S	P	S		S	S	T	S		E	D	E	N	S

PAGE 53

On Safari

IN OTHER WORDS
KIOSK

PAGE 55

Line Drawing

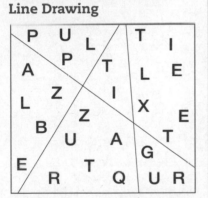

IT, RUG, PULP, BLAZE, QUARTZ, TEXTILE

THREE OF A KIND
THE BALLET SCHOOL HAD TO RELINQUISH A KEY DANCER TO STAGE *DELILAH AND SAMSON*.

PAGE 56

ABC

CITY SEARCH
LUMBER, NOBLER, NUMBER, RUMBLE, UNREEL

PAGE 57

In a Spin

PAGE 58

Tri-Color Maze

BETWEENER
LIST

PAGE 59

Puzzle Wiz

INITIAL REACTION
435 = MEMBERS of CONGRESS in the HOUSE of REPRESENTATIVES

PAGE 60

Find the Ships

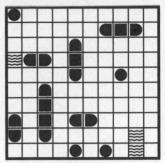

TWO-BY-FOUR
FOND, POUR; FUND, POOR; FORD, UPON; FOUR, POND

PAGE 61

Sudoku

1	2	7	3	6	9	4	5	8
3	6	5	4	8	1	2	9	7
9	4	8	2	7	5	6	3	1
5	8	4	1	9	6	3	7	2
6	9	2	7	5	3	1	8	4
7	3	1	8	2	4	5	6	9
2	5	6	9	1	8	7	4	3
4	1	9	6	3	7	8	2	5
8	7	3	5	4	2	9	1	6

MIXAGRAMS

L A U G H C U B E
E X U D E T R A M
F A C E T N U N S
T U B E R I N K Y

PAGE 62

Below the Belt

PAGE 63
Circular Reasoning

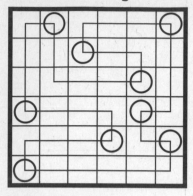

ADDITION SWITCH
5 0 9 + 2 9 4 = 8 0 3

PAGE 64
Triad Split Decisions

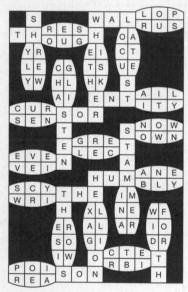

TRANSDELETION
DIETICIAN

PAGE 65
123

SUDOKU SUM
4 0 3 + 1 6 9 = 5 7 2

PAGE 66
Betting Setting

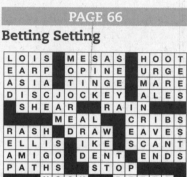

PAGE 67
Islands

AND SO ON
RANK and FILE

PAGE 68
The Green Stuff

COMMON SENSE
PRY

PAGE 69
Green Party

TONGUE TWISTER
MALAY

PAGE 70
Beastly Bunches

PAGE 71
One-Way Streets

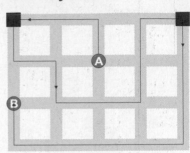

SOUND THINKING
TARTAR, TERRITORY, TRAITOR, TROTTER

PAGE 72
Hyper-Sudoku

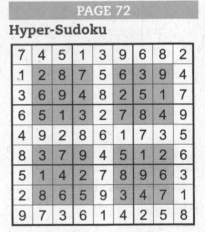

COUNTDOWN
98-7+6-54+3-2+1 = 45

PAGE 73
Star Search

TELEPHONE TRIOS
CHASSIS, STARTER, BATTERY

PAGE 74
School Subjects

PAGE 75
ABC

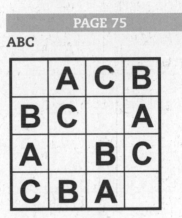

CLUELESS CROSSWORD

G	A	D	G	E	T	S
A		O		L		O
R	O	O	M	I	E	R
L		R		X		C
A	R	M	O	I	R	E
N		A		R		R
D	Y	N	A	S	T	Y

PAGE 76
Looped Path

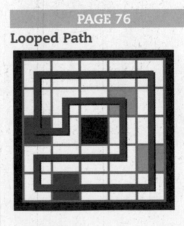

BETWEENER
HOME

PAGE 77
Sudoku

4	9	6	1	3	5	2	7	8
5	1	2	8	6	7	4	9	3
8	7	3	2	9	4	5	6	1
3	4	5	9	1	6	8	2	7
1	6	7	5	8	2	3	4	9
9	2	8	4	7	3	1	5	6
7	3	4	6	2	1	9	8	5
6	5	9	3	4	8	7	1	2
2	8	1	7	5	9	6	3	4

MIXAGRAMS
THEIR ARCS
PATIO MOSS
ARGUE FLAY
ODDLY MERE

PAGE 78
I Love a 49 Down

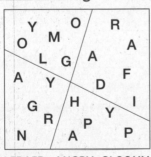

PAGE 79
Line Drawing

AFRAID, ANGRY, GLOOMY, HAPPY

THREE OF A KIND
THE REGATTA BEGAN IN THE HARBOR; ROWING IN HASTE, ALABAMA BEAT OBERLIN.

PAGE 80
Find the Ships

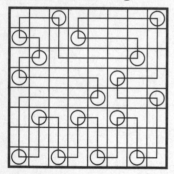

TWO-BY-FOUR
MUTE, TAIL (or ALIT); TAUT, LIME (or MILE)

PAGE 81
Circular Reasoning

ADDITION SWITCH
6 8 5 + 1 1 6 = 8 0 1

PAGE 82
Valentine's Day Gifts

O	K	L	A		W	A	R	M		F	R	A	M	E
U	N	I	T		E	L	I	A		E	A	S	E	L
R	O	M	A	N	T	I	C	D	I	N	N	E	R	S
S	T	A	G	E		A	H	E	M		C	A	V	E
		L	I	P	S		M	A	C	H				
N	O	S	A	L	E		G	O	N	E		H	E	M
A	T	T	N		E	T	O	N		D	R	O	N	E
C	H	O	C	O	L	A	T	E	H	E	A	R	T	S
H	E	L	E	N		K	A	Y	O		I	D	E	S
O	R	E		C	H	E	T		O	R	N	E	R	Y
		P	E	E	N		A	P	E	S				
A	L	A	I		R	O	A	R		A	T	A	L	L
B	O	U	Q	U	E	T	S	O	F	R	O	S	E	S
B	O	N	U	S		E	A	S	E		R	I	T	A
A	N	T	E	S		S	P	E	W		M	A	S	T

PAGE 83
Bead Maze

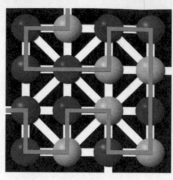

THREE AT A RHYME
JUICE, MOOSE, SPRUCE

PAGE 84
123

2	3	1	3	1	2	3	2	1
1	2	3	2	3	1	2	1	3
3	1	2	1	2	3	1	3	2
1	2	3	2	3	1	2	1	3
2	3	1	3	1	2	3	2	1
3	1	2	1	2	3	1	3	2
1	2	3	2	3	1	2	1	3
2	3	1	3	1	2	3	2	1
3	1	2	1	2	3	1	3	2

SUDOKU SUM
1 3 9 + 7 0 6 = 8 4 5

PAGE 85
Islands

AND SO ON
LAW and ORDER

PAGE 86
Anatomy 101

L	A	S	S	O		A	T	O	P		S	A	N	D
A	S	K	I	N		N	O	N	O		A	W	E	D
S	H	I	N	E		D	O	C	S		I	O	W	A
T	E	N		S	K	E	L	E	T	O	N	K	E	Y
	F	R	E	E	S				E	N	T	E	R	
P	O	L	I	C	E		C	O	R	K				
E	R	I	N		P	E	R	M		P	A	C	T	S
L	E	N	S		S	T	E	A	M		P	E	R	T
T	O	T	E	D		T	A	R	A		P	L	E	A
			I	T	E	M		G	A	L	L	E	Y	
	A	I	S	L	E		B	I	C	E	P			
M	U	S	C	L	E	B	E	A	C	H		H	O	E
I	D	L	E		O	U	R	S		I	V	O	R	Y
L	I	E	N		F	L	I	T		N	I	N	E	R
L	O	S	E		F	L	E	E		G	E	E	S	E

PAGE 87
Go With the Flow

COMMON SENSE
WIN

PAGE 88
Split Decisions

TRANSDELETION
SCREAM

PAGE 89

Hyper-Sudoku

9	5	1	8	6	7	2	3	4
6	7	2	1	4	3	5	9	8
3	4	8	9	5	2	6	7	1
2	6	5	3	9	8	4	1	7
7	9	3	4	1	6	8	5	2
1	8	4	2	7	5	3	6	9
5	1	9	6	8	4	7	2	3
4	3	7	5	2	9	1	8	6
8	2	6	7	3	1	9	4	5

MIXAGRAMS

S P A T E   W I L D
V I D E O   P U R R
C A B A L   H E R O
S P U R N   D E E P

PAGE 90

Load It Up

COAL · SACKS · EVEL
HALL · CRANE · RATE
ASIA · ALLEN · ANNE
RIGMAROLES · CAR
SNARL · LETGO
MELT · SALUTE
LASS · TARA · NAVAL
ITEM · BIB · DELI
DOMES · SEER · ERLE
SMILED · STEP
FLEET · TESTS
ALI · PICKUPTIME
LONE · ALLIN · EBAY
ORAL · REUSE · WIRE
TELL · TRESS · SATS

PAGE 91

Three-for-One Word Search

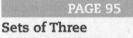

A Y C S R P K   Y O S D X N I
R O G R I V S   P R R Z E V D
B N E S M E Z   M A W E I R Q
I W C L I J O   A N R O C G H
L E D R P F H   J G L B L U E
S B A E T I H   L E A K O V U
X U L V A G Q   T R F B T E N

L D R I L L C
R E M M A H F
P J S M B S U
E L S I N V Y
K R A Z H T W
P D W N L C I
H Q G X E O A

IN OTHER WORDS
MIDTERM

PAGE 93

One-Way Streets

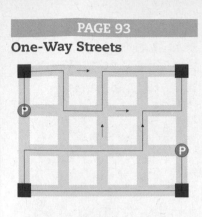

SOUND THINKING
HAPPILY, HOOPLA

PAGE 94

Georges

MAGMA · CLOD · NIKE
EPEES · HERO · ERIE
GERSHWINANDWILL
ARMS · ALAN · NESTS
HAND · GRAS
ROTATE · SEE · TSPS
EMILE · DIANA · TUE
GALLUPANDORWELL
ANT · PAIGE · REESE
LIST · IRS · GABLES
ABLY · PAYS
ABATE · FEES · IONS
CUSTERANDPATTON
TRIO · ARIA · HEIDI
INTO · MMDL · ASSET

PAGE 95

Sets of Three

THREE AT A RHYME
KNOT, WATT, YACHT

PAGE 96

Star Search

TELEPHONE TRIOS
CYMBALS, PICCOLO, UKULELE

PAGE 97

Triad Split Decisions

TRANSDELETION
POLLINATION

PAGE 98

Living Large

BAJA · CAGE · BEAMS
ALUM · ALAN · LALAW
RAMP · NONO · ASIDE
BIB · KINGSIZEBED
OWING · RESIDE
CAJOLE · POOR · SON
ALERT · DAWNS
RITE · REPLY · CBER
HEAPS · CHICO
SOP · EENY · FLAGON
INLUCK · PLANB
GIANTSLALOM · OFT
NOTSO · ASAP · DALI
ENTER · SHIP · IRAN
DYERS · HEDY · EDGY

PAGE 99

ABC

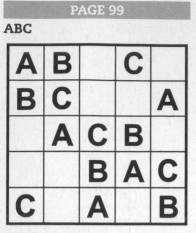

CITY SEARCH
GARBLED, REGALED

PAGE 100

Find the Ships

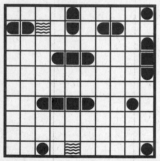

TWO-BY-FOUR
MAIN, CHOP; MOAN, CHIP

PAGE 101

Wise Guys

S	U	M	A	C		G	A	G	A		O	M	A	N
A	N	I	T	A		L	I	E	D		C	O	L	A
P	I	N	E	N	E	E	D	L	E		T	R	O	Y
			A	N	N	E		M	A	N	E	S		
S	T	R	A	P	I	N		T	R	I	N	I		
C	O	I	L	E	D		D	E	A	D	E	N	D	
R	O	B	E	S		P	E	S	C	I		G	I	G
U	K	E	S		S	U	I	T	E		S	H	O	E
B	U	Y		L	U	N	T	S		B	L	A	D	E
	P	E	N	A	L	T	Y		G	A	U	Z	E	S
	S	O	C	K	S		B	U	R	M	E	S	E	
S	A	T	B	Y		F	E	S	T					
O	L	E	O		R	I	D	E	H	E	R	D	O	N
A	T	A	D		E	R	I	C		N	O	I	S	E
P	O	K	Y		M	A	C	H		D	O	N	U	T

PAGE 102

Shamrock Maze

BETWEENER
SPACE

PAGE 103

Sudoku

6	1	2	8	4	3	7	9	5
3	8	7	9	6	5	2	1	4
4	9	5	2	7	1	3	8	6
2	7	8	4	5	6	1	3	9
5	4	9	1	3	8	6	7	2
1	3	6	7	2	9	5	4	8
7	2	1	6	8	4	9	5	3
8	6	3	5	9	7	4	2	1
9	5	4	3	1	2	8	6	7

MIXAGRAMS
K A P O K S E E K
S W A M I H O B O
T E N O N S E E N
S T U N G F R O G

PAGE 104

Circular Reasoning

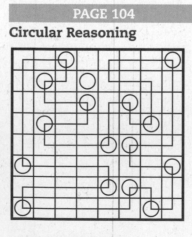

ADDITION SWITCH
4 5 8 + 2 4 3 = 7 0 1

PAGE 105

Hardware Store

B	L	O	B		H	T	T	P		P	I	T	C	H
E	I	R	E		I	O	W	A		O	C	A	L	A
R	E	A	L		A	T	A	T		T	E	X	A	S
G	U	L	L	Y	W	A	S	H	E	R		B	U	T
			M	E	A	L			H	O	A	R	S	E
I	N	F	A	N	T		C	A	S	A	B	A		
C	A	I	N		H	O	U	R		S	E	C	T	S
U	P	N		F	A	N	B	E	L	T		K	O	P
S	E	G	A	L		M	E	S	A		J	E	F	E
	E	L	U	D	E	D		S	T	A	T	U	E	
T	E	R	E	S	A		A	V	O	W				
A	N	N		T	H	U	N	D	E	R	B	O	L	T
S	U	A	V	E		M	O	O	G		O	P	I	E
T	R	I	E	R		P	A	R	A		N	A	M	E
Y	E	L	L	S		S	H	E	S		E	L	A	N

PAGE 106

Islands

Island grid with 1, 2, 3, 4 clues.

AND SO ON
HEART and SOUL

PAGE 107

Hyper-Sudoku

7	6	8	3	1	9	4	2	5
3	2	5	6	7	4	9	8	1
4	9	1	8	5	2	3	7	6
8	4	3	7	2	1	6	5	9
6	1	9	4	8	5	7	3	2
2	5	7	9	3	6	8	1	4
1	3	6	2	9	7	5	4	8
5	8	4	1	6	3	2	9	7
9	7	2	5	4	8	1	6	3

COUNTDOWN
9+87-65-4-3-21 = 3

PAGE 108
Ways to Pay

E	G	G	S		V	I	B	E	S		T	A	S	S
B	O	A	T		A	D	O	R	E		I	N	C	A
B	O	L	A		D	E	L	I	A		E	T	O	N
	P	A	R	T	I	A	L	C	R	E	D	I	T	
		T	E	M				S	T	Y				
T	O	R	R	E		M	I	A		H	E	A	R	T
I	S	E	E		B	O	N	S	A	I		M	E	A
B	A	C	K	G	R	O	U	N	D	C	H	E	C	K
E	G	O		H	O	R	S	E	S		A	N	T	E
R	E	N	T	A		E	E	R		A	R	D	O	R
		A	N	A				S	A	D				
	C	A	V	A	L	R	Y	C	H	A	R	G	E	
C	O	V	E		L	E	V	E	E		O	A	R	S
O	D	O	R		O	N	E	N	D		C	L	I	O
D	A	W	N		T	E	S	T	S		K	E	E	N

PAGE 109
Three-for-One Word Search

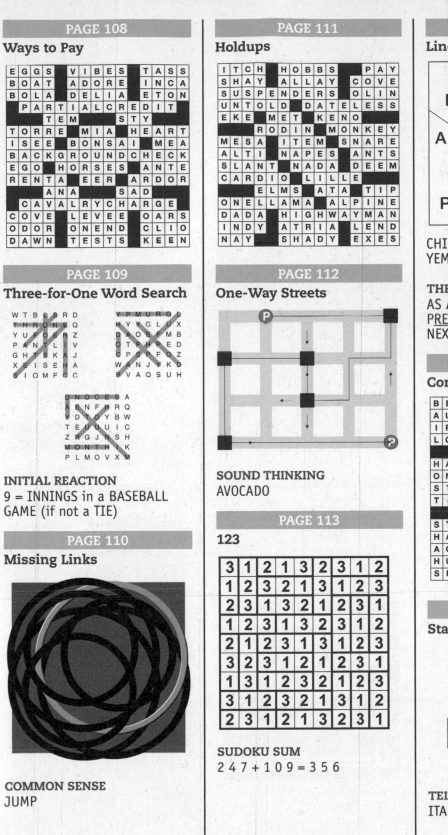

W T B L S R D
T H R O N E Q
Y U F O E R Z
P A N T L I V
G H T S K A J
X E I S E H A
S I O M F C C

Y P M U R G L
H Y Y G L U X
D A O E F M B
O T P H R E D
C P G P F O Z
W A N J Y K D
B V A Q S U H

D N O C E S A
A E N F H R Q
V D T O Y B W
T E U U U I C
Z R G J N S H
M O N T H I K
P L M O V X M

INITIAL REACTION
9 = INNINGS in a BASEBALL GAME (if not a TIE)

PAGE 110
Missing Links

COMMON SENSE
JUMP

PAGE 111
Holdups

I	T	C	H		H	O	B	B	S			P	A	Y
S	H	A	Y		A	L	L	A	Y		C	O	V	E
S	U	S	P	E	N	D	E	R	S		O	L	I	N
U	N	T	O	L	D		D	A	T	E	L	E	S	S
E	K	E		M	E	T		K	E	N	O			
			R	O	D	I	N			M	O	N	K	E	Y
M	E	S	A		I	T	E	M		S	N	A	R	E
A	L	T	I		N	A	P	E	S		A	N	T	S
S	L	A	N	T		N	A	D	A		D	E	E	M
C	A	R	D	I	O		L	I	L	L	E			
		E	L	M	S		A	T	A		T	I	P	
O	N	E	L	L	A	M	A		A	L	P	I	N	E
D	A	D	A		H	I	G	H	W	A	Y	M	A	N
I	N	D	Y		A	T	R	I	A		L	E	N	D
N	A	Y			S	H	A	D	Y		E	X	E	S

PAGE 112
One-Way Streets

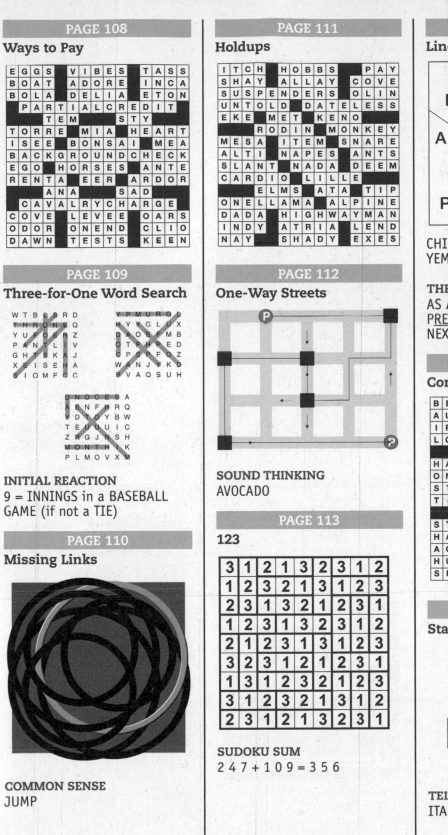

SOUND THINKING
AVOCADO

PAGE 113
123

3	1	2	1	3	2	3	1	2
1	2	3	2	1	3	1	2	3
2	3	1	3	2	1	2	3	1
1	2	3	1	3	2	3	1	2
2	1	2	3	1	3	1	2	3
3	2	3	1	2	1	2	3	1
1	3	1	2	3	2	1	2	3
3	1	2	3	2	1	3	1	2
2	3	1	2	1	3	2	3	1

SUDOKU SUM
247 + 109 = 356

PAGE 114
Line Drawing

CHILE, CHINA, INDIA, JAPAN, YEMEN

THREE OF A KIND
AS A PSYCHIC DRE<u>AMER, I CAN</u> <u>PR</u>EDICT EVENTS A<u>CROSS</u> THE NEXT DIMENSION.

PAGE 115
Completely

B	E	E	T		H	I	S	S		B	A	L	E	S
A	U	R	A		E	C	O	N		U	R	I	A	H
I	R	I	S		H	I	L	O		M	I	S	S	Y
L	O	C	K	T	H	E	D	O	O	R		T	E	L
			H	E	R		T	O	A		S	L	Y	
H	A	L	V	A	H		I	M	P	S				
O	N	I	O	N		W	E	E	P		P	E	R	U
S	T	O	C	K	T	H	E	S	H	E	L	V	E	S
T	I	N	A		H	I	L	T		L	A	I	N	E
			B	R	E	T			T	I	T	L	E	D
S	T	P		O	D	E		P	A	Z				
H	A	R		B	A	R	R	E	L	A	L	O	N	G
A	G	I	L	E		A	U	T	O		O	V	E	N
H	U	M	O	R		T	E	E	N		S	E	R	A
S	P	E	N	T			S	S	R	S		T	R	O	T

PAGE 116
Star Search

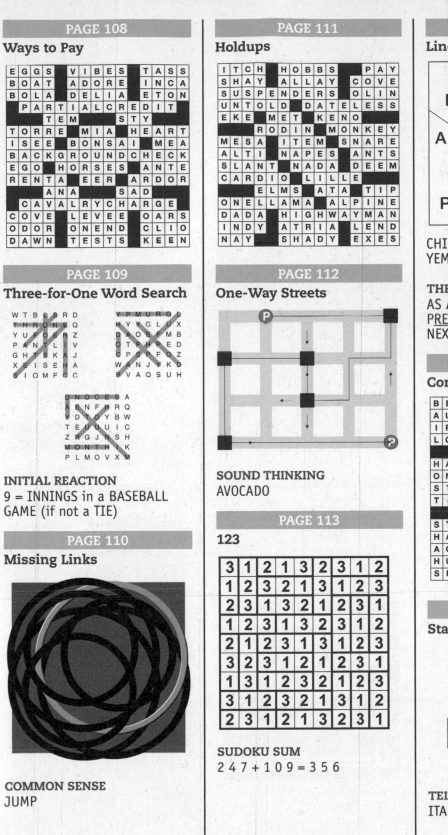

TELEPHONE TRIOS
ITALIAN, SPANISH, MALTESE

PAGE 117
Straight Ahead

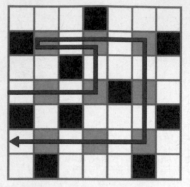

THREE AT A RHYME
BIRD, HEARD, WORD

PAGE 118
Straighten Up

C	O	O	P		A	L	V	A			I	S	M	S

PAGE 119
Hyper-Sudoku

3	5	9	8	1	4	6	7	2
6	2	4	3	7	9	5	8	1
8	1	7	5	2	6	3	4	9
5	9	8	6	3	1	7	2	4
4	7	1	2	5	8	9	3	6
2	3	6	9	4	7	8	1	5
9	4	5	1	8	3	2	6	7
1	8	2	7	6	5	4	9	3
7	6	3	4	9	2	1	5	8

MIXAGRAMS

FLIER JUDO
UNLIT PLEA
LOTUS PUCE
LIMBO CAKE

PAGE 120
ABC

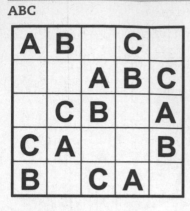

CITY SEARCH
DEMOTION, DEVOTION,
MOTIONED

PAGE 121
Baker's Quartet

PAGE 122
Tri-Color Maze

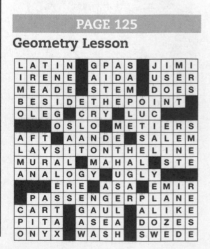

BETWEENER
TRAP

PAGE 123
Find the Ships

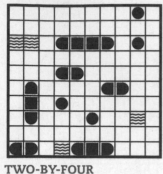

TWO-BY-FOUR
GAZE, MAIN; MAZE, GAIN

PAGE 124
Triad Split Decisions

TRANSDELETION
STILETTO

PAGE 125
Geometry Lesson

L	A	T	I	N		G	P	A	S		J	I	M	I
I	R	E	N	E		A	I	D	A		U	S	E	R
M	E	A	D	E		S	T	E	M		D	O	E	S
B	E	S	I	D	E	T	H	E	P	O	I	N	T	
O	L	E	G		C	R	Y		L	U	C			
			O	S	L	O		M	E	T	I	E	R	S
A	F	T		A	A	N	D	E		S	A	L	E	M
L	A	Y	S	I	T	O	N	T	H	E	L	I	N	E
M	U	R	A	L		M	A	H	A	L		S	T	E
A	N	A	L	O	G	Y		U	G	L	Y			
			E	R	E		A	S	A		E	M	I	R
	P	A	S	S	E	N	G	E	R	P	L	A	N	E
C	A	R	T		G	A	U	L		A	L	I	K	E
P	I	T	A		A	S	E	A		D	O	Z	E	S
O	N	Y	X		W	A	S	H		S	W	E	D	E

PAGE 126

123

2	1	3	1	3	2	3	2	1
1	2	1	3	2	3	1	3	2
3	1	3	2	1	2	3	2	1
2	3	2	1	3	1	2	1	3
3	1	3	2	1	2	1	3	2
1	2	1	3	2	3	2	1	3
2	3	2	1	3	1	3	2	1
3	2	1	2	1	3	1	3	2
1	3	2	3	2	1	2	1	3

SUDOKU SUM
5 1 4 + 2 9 3 = 8 0 7

PAGE 127

Circular Reasoning

ADDITION SWITCH
1 7 8 + 2 6 7 = 4 4 5

PAGE 128

Utility Players

R	O	A	R		L	A	D	E	S		T	W	I	G
O	R	C	A		A	V	I	L	A		D	A	N	A
B	A	R	N		B	A	S	I	L		S	T	A	T
E	L	E	C	T	R	I	C	E	E	L		E	W	E
		H	E	A	L			S	A	C	R	E	D	
R	E	G	E	N	T		P	O	M	P	O	M		
O	P	A	R	T		P	A	P	A		T	E	R	I
L	E	S		H	E	A	V	E	N	S		L	O	N
L	E	S	S		B	R	E	D		A	L	O	O	F
		T	I	M	B	E	R		P	R	O	N	T	O
M	E	A	N	I	T		C	L	A	W				
A	N	T		O	I	L	P	A	I	N	T	I	N	G
S	T	I	R		D	O	O	N	E		E	D	I	E
T	R	O	Y		E	L	M	E	R		C	E	N	T
S	Y	N	E		S	L	E	D	S		H	A	A	S

PAGE 129

Red-Blue-Red

COMMON SENSE
THIN

PAGE 131

Dive Right In

TONGUE TWISTER
HEBREW

PAGE 132

Hyper-Sudoku

7	3	5	2	6	4	8	1	9
6	2	8	1	5	9	7	3	4
1	9	4	7	3	8	6	5	2
9	5	6	3	7	1	2	4	8
4	7	1	8	2	6	3	9	5
2	8	3	9	4	5	1	6	7
5	1	7	4	8	3	9	2	6
3	6	2	5	9	7	4	8	1
8	4	9	6	1	2	5	7	3

MIXAGRAMS

R O O S T   A B L Y
A P T L Y   T O R N
C A R O M   M A U L
P R A W N   A T O P

PAGE 133

Hot Stuff

T	O	L	E	T		Q	U	A	S	H		J	E	T
I	M	A	G	E		T	R	I	T	E		A	X	E
R	A	N	G	E	F	I	N	D	E	R		W	I	N
E	N	D		N	A	P	S		O	U	S	T	S	
		H	E	A	D			D	A	I	S			
	F	O	R	G	E	O	N	E	S	N	A	M	E	
O	L	L	I	E		P	A	S	S	E		U	L	M
W	I	D	E		B	E	N	I	N		A	S	E	A
N	N	E		C	O	R	A	L		A	L	I	C	E
	G	R	I	L	L	A	S	U	S	P	E	C	T	
		K	I	D	S			A	P	E	S			
D	O	Z	E	N		B	A	B	A		T	W	A	
E	V	A		I	R	O	N	C	U	R	T	A	I	N
P	A	N		C	E	D	A	R		E	R	N	S	T
P	L	Y		S	A	D	I	E		L	A	D	E	S

PAGE 134

One-Way Streets

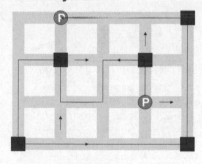

SOUND THINKING
POSTERITY, UPSTART

PAGE 135

Star Search

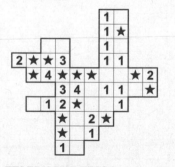

TELEPHONE TRIOS
ACROBAT, GYMNAST, JUGGLER

PAGE 136
What a Racket

```
S T E M   M O S S       M R I S
W A L E   O R C H   J A U N T
A X E D   N C A R   A I M T O
G I V I N G A B U Z Z     B E N
      C I R     G A Z E L L E
J U B I L E E S   P U R E
E T A   E L L E S     P O S E R
A N N E     S L E E P   S E R E
N E G R I   A I R E D   A T F
    A L L Y   N A R R A T E S
J E W E L E D     O A T
A T A     B A R K E X T R A C T
W H Y M E   Y E T I   E Q U I
E N A C T     A R O D   S U E T
D O T S     S I N E     T A R O
```

PAGE 137
Go With the Flow

THREE AT A RHYME
FOLK, OAK, SPOKE

PAGE 138
Sudoku

8	3	2	4	5	9	1	6	7
1	6	7	2	8	3	5	9	4
5	4	9	1	6	7	3	8	2
7	2	3	6	4	5	9	1	8
9	8	5	3	2	1	7	4	6
4	1	6	7	9	8	2	5	3
6	7	8	5	1	2	4	3	9
2	5	4	9	3	6	8	7	1
3	9	1	8	7	4	6	2	5

COUNTDOWN
98-7-65+43+21 = 90

PAGE 139
Hits and Misses

```
G R A B   A R E A S       S T A N
N E H I   B U T C H   O H N O
A L E C   R I A T A   B E G S
W O M A N I N L O V E     T I E
      R I D     R E X R E E D
C A B B A G E S   S T E M
A M I     E G A D   R I P E N
G I R L F R O M I P A N E M A
E S T E E   S O A R   S I P
  H E R B   A N I S E T T E
F O R S A L E     M A X
U N I     L A D Y M A D O N N A
S I G N   S W E E T   T E E S
E C H O   T I T L E   I M O K
S E T S     S N I T S   C O N S
```

PAGE 140
Split Decisions

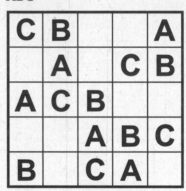

TRANSDELETION
RAIN MAN

PAGE 141
Islands

Grid with numbers: 4, 3, 2 (top row), 4 (middle right), 1 (bottom left).

AND SO ON
WAYS and MEANS

PAGE 142
Sounds Like a Plan

```
L A W N   C L A S P       M A C H
O P I E   Y A L T A   E S A U
G A R D E N P L O T   T I R E
I C E   R I D     O R C H A R D
C E D R I C   S L O M O
      H E I S T     L O D G E D
W A R Y     S H A G   N A I V E
E X A M   M E L E E   C L E F
A L I E N   D E N Y   T A R T
      C A B O T     S H R I K E
H I G H T O P     P I E   G E L
I D L E   D E S I G N F L A W
T E E M   E R I C H   B O N E
S A N E     S A D A T   I O U S
```

PAGE 143
ABC

C	B			A
	A		C	B
A	C	B		
	A	B	C	
B		C	A	

CLUELESS CROSSWORD

```
V I A D U C T
A   P   N   H
N U R T U R E
D   I   S   A
A C C O U N T
L   O   A   E
S E T T L E R
```

PAGE 144
Four-Letter Word Routes

BETWEENER
APPLE

PAGE 145
Line Drawing

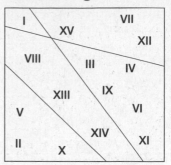

The roman numerals in each region are written with the same number of straight lines.

THREE OF A KIND
I AM IN DOUBT OUR GOVERNMENT WOULD BE ABLE TO CALL THE PORTUGUESE DIPLOMAT "TERSE."

PAGE 146
Getting an Assist

S	C	R	A	M		T	A	R	T		A	H	A	B
E	R	I	C	A		A	S	E	A		D	I	V	A
A	I	D	E	D	E	C	A	M	P		A	R	E	A
T	E	E		I	W	O	N		W	A	G	E	R	S
O	R	R		G	E	M		G	A	P	E	D		
		P	A	R	A	S	I	T	E		H	E	N	
A	P	R	O	N		A	V	E	R	S	E	T	O	
M	A	I	L		P	O	L	E	R		A	L	A	N
A	N	G	O	L	A	N	S			A	M	P	L	E
N	T	H		E	S	C	A	P	A	D	E			
		T	H	O	S	E		I	S	H		S	A	P
A	T	H	E	N	A		A	L	O	E		U	M	A
C	H	A	D		G	I	R	L	F	R	I	D	A	Y
T	A	N	G		E	T	T	A		E	R	A	S	E
S	I	D	E		S	T	E	R		S	E	N	S	E

PAGE 147
Find the Ships

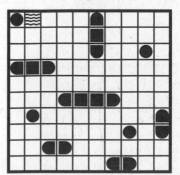

TWO-BY-FOUR
HUNT, LAZE (or ZEAL)

PAGE 148
Hyper-Sudoku

5	6	4	9	3	2	7	8	1
2	8	9	4	1	7	5	3	6
7	3	1	6	5	8	9	2	4
9	7	5	2	8	1	6	4	3
6	2	8	3	4	5	1	9	7
1	4	3	7	6	9	8	5	2
3	9	2	8	7	6	4	1	5
4	1	6	5	9	3	2	7	8
8	5	7	1	2	4	3	6	9

MIXAGRAMS

A	P	I	S	H		S	O	D	A
L	U	N	G	E		A	V	I	D
A	N	G	E	L		P	E	S	T
H	O	U	N	D		T	R	A	Y

PAGE 149
True Grit

A	H	E	M		O	R	B	S		R	A	D	A	R
H	E	X	A		P	O	R	T		A	Q	A	B	A
A	M	O	R		E	S	A	U		D	U	R	U	M
	P	R	I	N	C	E	V	A	L	I	A	N	T	
		B	O	P		H	O	R	A	C	E			
R	O	I		R	B	I		T	B	A		A	L	I
A	R	T	Y		E	P	A		C	L	A	M	O	R
F	E	A	R	L	E	S	S	F	O	S	D	I	C	K
T	O	N	S	I	L		P	I	A		S	A	K	E
S	S	T		F	I	B		R	T	E		B	E	D
		R	E	N	A	M	E		C	C	I			
	B	R	A	V	E	N	E	W	W	O	R	L	D	
B	A	I	Z	E		T	R	O	Y		E	I	R	E
O	L	M	O	S		E	C	O	L		S	T	O	W
A	L	E	R	T		R	I	D	E		T	Y	P	E

PAGE 150
Circular Reasoning

ADDITION SWITCH
6 3 9 + 1 6 9 = 8 0 8

PAGE 151
Turn Maze

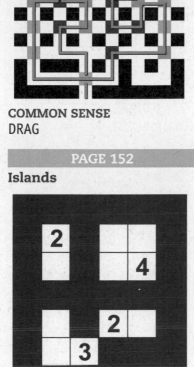

COMMON SENSE
DRAG

PAGE 152
Islands

An illustration with numbers: 2, 4, 2, 3.

AND SO ON
SAVINGS and LOAN

PAGE 153
See Shells

A	L	E	C		L	E	G	A	L		E	C	H	O
C	A	L	L		A	R	U	B	A		B	R	A	M
E	M	M	A		C	R	A	B	N	E	B	U	L	A
	B	O	M	B	E		M	A	D	D		Z	E	N
		D	O	W	D		S	H	I	V				
R	A	I	N	I	E	R		O	C	E	A	N	S	
M	I	N	G		N	C	O	S		T	A	G	U	P
A	G	O	G		G	O	B	A	D		L	A	D	E
M	E	D	E	A		R	I	L	E		S	T	E	W
A	L	E	R	T	S		N	O	V	I	C	E	S	
			S	I	C	S		N	O	R	A			
A	R	C		L	O	P	E		T	E	L	L	S	
T	U	R	N	T	U	R	T	L	E		L	U	N	G
O	B	O	E		R	E	T	I	E		O	B	I	E
N	E	W	T		S	E	A	L	S		P	E	P	E

PAGE 154

123

1	2	3	1	2	3	2	1	3
3	1	2	3	1	2	1	3	2
2	3	1	2	3	1	2	1	3
3	1	2	3	1	2	3	2	1
1	2	3	1	2	3	1	3	2
2	3	1	2	3	1	3	2	1
3	1	2	3	1	3	2	1	2
2	3	1	2	3	2	1	3	1
1	2	3	1	2	1	3	2	3

SUDOKU SUM
3 7 8 + 2 1 6 = 5 9 4

PAGE 155

Find the Ships

TWO-BY-FOUR
GIFT, HURL

PAGE 156

Cattle Call

J	E	R	K		G	P	A	S		R	A	M	E	N
A	S	I	A		E	R	I	E		U	B	O	A	T
M	A	L	E		N	O	R	M		N	Y	M	P	H
B	U	L	L	S	E	S	S	I	O	N	S			
		O	R	E			R	E	S	E	T	S		
N	E	P	A	L	I		B	O	E	R		S	U	P
A	X	E	L		C	A	L	F	M	U	S	C	L	E
S	P	E	E	R		B	A	M		P	S	H	A	W
C	O	W	C	A	T	C	H	E	R		R	E	N	E
A	S	E		R	O	S	S		A	N	S	W	E	R
R	E	E	L	I	N			O	N	E				
			S	T	E	E	R	C	L	E	A	R	O	F
L	A	N	A	I		G	A	E	A		M	O	I	L
E	L	I	T	E		G	N	A	T		P	O	L	E
G	L	A	S	S		S	I	N	E		S	T	Y	X

PAGE 157

Writers Jigsaw

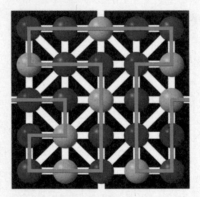

IN OTHER WORDS
GOSLING

PAGE 158

Bead Maze

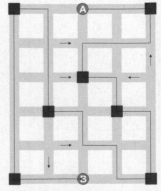

THREE AT A RHYME
LEI, SWAY, WHEY

PAGE 159

Star Search

```
          ★       ★
      3 ★ 4   3
      1   ★   ★ ★
  1 ★   2   3
  1   1   ★ 2       1
  1   3 ★       ★
  1 ★ 2 ★   3   2 ★ 2
      2   ★ ★
        1   2
        1 ★
```

TELEPHONE TRIOS
MONTANA, VERMONT, WYOMING

PAGE 160

Pronounced Differences

P	I	N	T	A		A	N	T	E		S	T	L	O
A	N	A	I	S		M	A	R	X		T	H	O	U
C	O	U	G	H	S	Y	R	U	P		U	R	L	S
E	N	T	R	E	E		C	E	E		D	O	L	T
		I	S	T	O		D	R	S	E	U	S	S	
O	P	T	S		O	P	S		T	A	N	G		
R	O	O		U	R	A	L			O	T	H	E	R
S	O	U	S		T	A	T	A	R		S	P	R	Y
O	H	G	E	E		H	O	Y	A		U	L	E	
		H	A	T	S		N	E	D		R	T	E	S
S	A	B	B	A	T	H		R	I	L	E			
E	B	R	O		A	O	L		S	A	H	A	R	A
D	O	E	R		D	O	U	G	H	M	I	X	E	R
G	I	A	N		I	C	K	Y		B	R	O	N	C
E	L	K	E		A	H	E	M		S	E	N	D	S

PAGE 161

Sudoku

2	1	9	4	8	6	7	3	5
8	4	7	1	5	3	9	2	6
3	6	5	7	9	2	1	8	4
6	3	8	5	4	7	2	9	1
9	5	2	6	3	1	4	7	8
4	7	1	8	2	9	5	6	3
5	9	4	3	7	8	6	1	2
7	8	6	2	1	5	3	4	9
1	2	3	9	6	4	8	5	7

MIXAGRAMS
E T H I C   S T A Y
S K I E R   O I L Y
A R G U E   O D D S
U S H E R   M E O W

PAGE 162

One-Way Streets

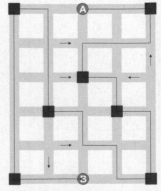

SOUND THINKING
DIAGNOSE

PAGE 163

ABC

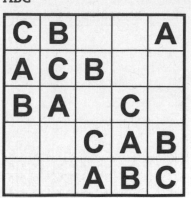

CITY SEARCH
MEASURE

PAGE 164

The Old Sod

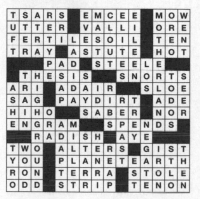

PAGE 165

Twelve-Letter Word

BETWEENER
DROP

PAGE 166

Find the Ships

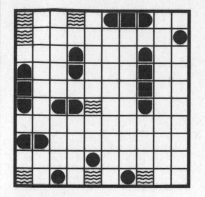

TWO-BY-FOUR
EPIC, VEER (or EVER); VICE, PEER

PAGE 167

123

3	1	3	2	1	2	1	2	3
2	3	2	1	3	1	3	1	2
1	2	1	3	2	3	2	3	1
2	1	3	1	3	2	1	2	3
3	2	1	3	2	1	3	1	2
2	1	3	2	1	3	2	3	1
1	3	2	1	3	2	3	1	2
3	2	1	2	1	3	1	2	3
1	3	2	3	2	1	2	3	1

SUDOKU SUM
3 8 5 + 4 0 6 = 7 9 1

PAGE 169

Brooklynese

S	H	R	E	D		S	L	O	B		D	A	L	I
H	E	A	V	E		P	E	R	U		E	D	E	N
A	R	N	E	L		E	V	I	L		P	L	O	T
D	E	T	R	A	I	N	I	N	G		R	E	N	E
		N	O	T		G	E	N	E	R	A	L		
H	O	L	D	O	N		D	E	S					
O	D	I	E		I	C	O	N		A	S	I	D	E
P	O	O	L		C	A	R	E	S		I	D	E	A
E	R	N	I	E		N	E	W	T		N	L	E	R
		G	P	A			E	D	G	E	R	S		
T	H	E	H	I	L	L		O	N	E				
H	E	A	T		D	E	F	R	O	S	T	I	N	G
A	N	T	I		R	A	I	D		P	A	T	I	O
W	R	E	N		I	S	L	E		O	R	A	T	E
S	I	N	G		N	E	E	R		T	A	L	E	S

PAGE 170

Circular Reasoning

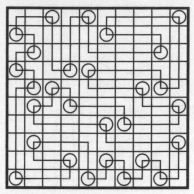

ADDITION SWITCH
5 1 8 + 3 8 6 = 9 0 4

PAGE 171

Islands

AND SO ON
DOLLARS and CENTS

PAGE 172

Energy Boost

P	O	K	E	S		T	R	U	S	T		W	A	D
A	B	A	S	H		H	A	V	E	N		E	L	I
W	E	L	C	O	M	E	M	E	A	T		N	S	A
E	S	E		P	E	N	P	A	L		A	T	O	Z
R	E	L	A	P	S	E			A	P	B	S		
		N	E	A	T	K	I	N	G	C	O	L	E	
A	S	K	E	D		E	S	T	A		U	A	W	
C	H	A	W		B	A	L	M	S		E	T	T	E
O	A	T		M	A	I	L			O	T	H	E	R
W	H	E	A	T	S	M	Y	L	I	N	E			
	S	A	V	E			A	G	E	S	A	G	O	
P	U	M	A		B	E	A	C	O	N		B	R	A
A	R	I		V	A	M	P	I	R	E	B	E	A	T
P	I	T		E	L	I	S	E		S	Y	L	P	H
A	S	H		E	L	L	E	R		S	E	L	E	S

PAGE 173
Tri-Color Maze

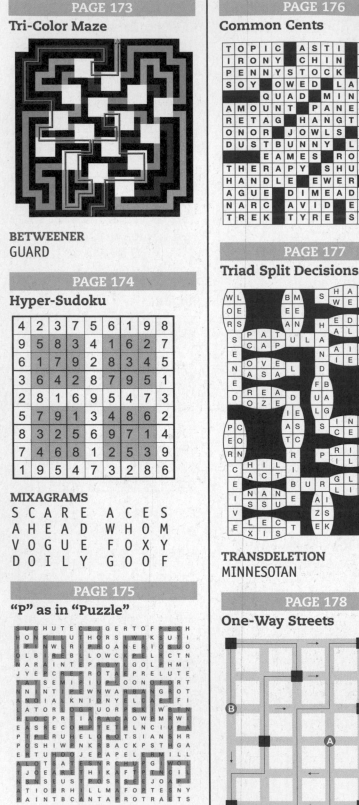

BETWEENER
GUARD

PAGE 174
Hyper-Sudoku

4	2	3	7	5	6	1	9	8
9	5	8	3	4	1	6	2	7
6	1	7	9	2	8	3	4	5
3	6	4	2	8	7	9	5	1
2	8	1	6	9	5	4	7	3
5	7	9	1	3	4	8	6	2
8	3	2	5	6	9	7	1	4
7	4	6	8	1	2	5	3	9
1	9	5	4	7	3	2	8	6

MIXAGRAMS

```
S C A R E    A C E S
A H E A D    W H O M
V O G U E    F O X Y
D O I L Y    G O O F
```

PAGE 175
"P" as in "Puzzle"

INITIAL REACTION
1 = WHEELS on a UNICYCLE

PAGE 176
Common Cents

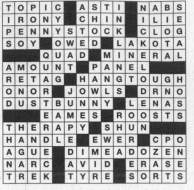

T	O	P	I	C		A	S	T	I		N	A	B	S
I	R	O	N	Y		C	H	I	N		I	L	I	E
P	E	N	N	Y	S	T	O	C	K		C	L	O	G
S	O	Y		O	W	E	D		L	A	K	O	T	A
			Q	U	A	D		M	I	N	E	R	A	L
A	M	O	U	N	T		P	A	N	E	L			
R	E	T	A	G		H	A	N	G	T	O	U	G	H
O	N	O	R		J	O	W	L	S		D	R	N	O
D	U	S	T	B	U	N	N	Y		L	E	N	A	S
			E	A	M	E	S		R	O	O	S	T	S
T	H	E	R	A	P	Y		S	H	U	N			
H	A	N	D	L	E		E	W	E	R		C	P	O
A	G	U	E		D	I	M	E	A	D	O	Z	E	N
N	A	R	C		A	V	I	D		E	R	A	S	E
T	R	E	K		T	Y	R	E		S	O	R	T	S

PAGE 177
Triad Split Decisions

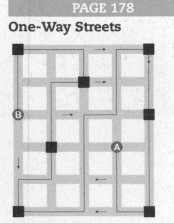

TRANSDELETION
MINNESOTAN

PAGE 178
One-Way Streets

SOUND THINKING
ANALOGY, KNOWLEDGE

PAGE 179
How Easy Is It?

H	I	T	S		A	C	R	E		M	A	D	A	M
O	M	E	N		L	O	A	N		E	L	A	T	E
N	A	N	U		B	O	Z	O		L	I	B	R	A
C	R	A	B	C	A	K	E	S		T	A	C	I	T
H	E	N	B	A	N	E		M	E	S	H			
O	T	T	E	R		R	E	D	I	D		I	L	L
			D	O	W		P	U	T		C	E	O	
A	I	L		B	A	B	C	O	C	K		K	I	X
F	R	A		S	R	O		H	E	E				
T	A	B		S	T	A	T	E		A	N	T	A	S
		C	R	E	E		S	A	N	G	R	I	A	
S	P	O	O	N		A	B	C	O	U	L	O	M	B
L	E	A	S	T		N	E	A	R		I	P	S	E
A	S	T	E	R		K	E	P	T		S	P	A	R
M	O	S	S	Y		A	R	E	A		H	O	T	S

PAGE 180
Dicey

COMMON SENSE
BOOKS

PAGE 181
Star Search

TELEPHONE TRIOS
CHARIOT, SCOOTER, TAXICAB

PAGE 182

Sudoku

8	5	6	9	1	3	4	2	7
4	1	2	7	6	8	3	5	9
9	3	7	5	4	2	6	1	8
7	8	9	2	5	6	1	3	4
1	6	3	8	9	4	5	7	2
5	2	4	1	3	7	9	8	6
6	7	1	4	2	5	8	9	3
2	4	5	3	8	9	7	6	1
3	9	8	6	7	1	2	4	5

COUNTDOWN
9-8+7-6+5+43-21 = 29

PAGE 183

Drive Line

PAGE 184

ABC

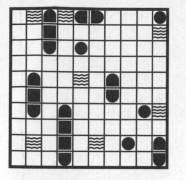

CLUELESS CROSSWORD

PAGE 185

Find the Ships

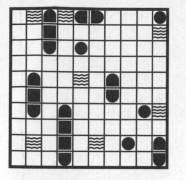

TWO-BY-FOUR
VAIN, LILY

PAGE 186

Dejected

PAGE 187

Blue-Red-Blue

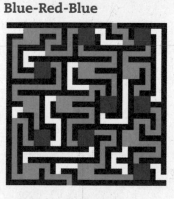

THREE AT A RHYME
CREPES, SHAPES, TRAIPSE

PAGE 188

123

1	3	2	1	2	3	1	3	2
2	1	3	2	3	1	2	1	3
1	2	1	3	2	3	1	3	2
3	1	3	2	1	2	3	2	1
1	3	2	1	2	3	2	1	3
3	2	1	3	1	2	3	2	1
2	3	2	1	3	1	2	1	3
3	2	1	3	1	2	1	3	2
2	1	3	2	3	1	3	2	1

SUDOKU SUM
5 0 4 + 1 7 9 = 6 8 3

PAGE 189

Circular Reasoning

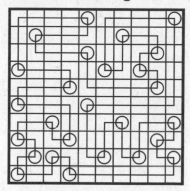

ADDITION SWITCH
6 7 6 + 2 3 5 = 9 1 1

PAGE 190

Middle Management

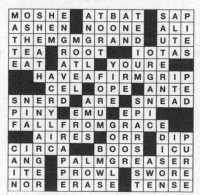

PAGE 191
Hyper-Sudoku

1	4	8	3	9	7	5	6	2
2	7	6	4	5	1	8	3	9
3	5	9	8	6	2	4	7	1
7	2	3	1	8	5	6	9	4
6	9	5	2	3	4	1	8	7
8	1	4	9	7	6	2	5	3
4	3	7	5	2	8	9	1	6
9	8	2	6	1	3	7	4	5
5	6	1	7	4	9	3	2	8

MIXAGRAMS

NOVEL ABUT
AGONY PLUG
VICAR DUNE
YIELD MERE

PAGE 192
Split Decisions

TRANSDELETION
CANTEEN

PAGE 193
Impact Statements

C	A	M	P		S	T	A	L	E		A	P	B	S
A	L	I	A		T	I	L	E	S		Q	U	I	P
P	I	G	I	N	A	P	O	K	E		U	N	T	O
		R	O	B	O	T	S		L	A	C	T	O	
O	N	E	S	E	L	F		R	U	S	H	E	R	
T	E	L		L	E	F	T	J	A	B		B	R	S
R	E	B	A		R	O	M	E	R	O				
A	D	O	S		C	R	A	G	S		I	A	M	B
	W	H	I	P	U	P				B	R	E	R	
E	R	G		B	U	M	P	E	R	S		D	N	A
N	E	R	V	E	S		L	U	M	P	S	U	M	
I	C	E	A	X		S	E	A	B	E	E			
G	O	A	L		C	A	T	T	L	E	P	R	O	D
M	U	S	E		A	G	R	E	E		P	E	A	R
A	P	E	S		D	E	E	D	S		Y	A	K	S

PAGE 194
Brain Coral Maze

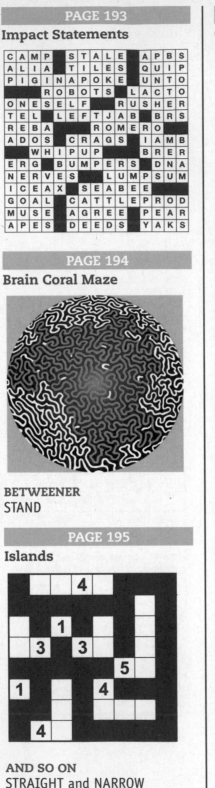

BETWEENER
STAND

PAGE 195
Islands

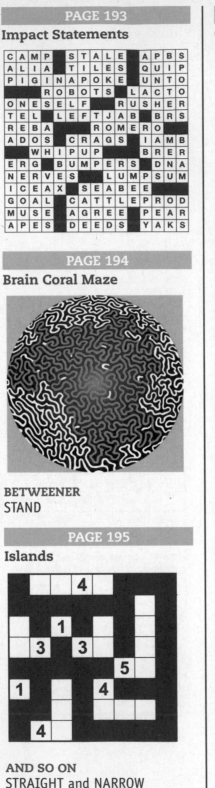

AND SO ON
STRAIGHT and NARROW

PAGE 196
One-Way Streets

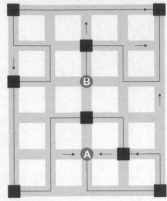

SOUND THINKING
FAIRNESS, FURNACE

PAGE 197
Hi, Sweetie

C	M	X	I		M	A	L	T		F	E	T	C	H
Z	E	E	S		E	L	I	E		L	A	U	R	A
E	T	N	A		T	I	E	R		A	S	N	E	W
C	O	O	K	I	E	B	U	M	S	T	E	A	D	
H	O	N		H	O	I		I	T	S		S	I	N
	A	E	R		S	N	O		R	A	T	E		
A	M	E	B	A		K	H	A	N		A	L	O	E
S	U	G	A	R	R	A	Y	L	E	O	N	A	R	D
S	S	R	S		U	T	E	S		S	U	D	S	Y
A	T	E	E		M	E	R		S	A	P			
D	A	G		A	B	S		E	E	K		U	M	P
	C	I	N	N	A	M	O	N	C	A	R	T	E	R
S	H	O	O	T		I	N	T	O		E	U	R	O
R	E	U	S	E		T	E	E	N		B	R	I	M
A	S	S	E	S		H	A	R	D		A	N	T	S

PAGE 198
Sudoku

7	1	9	5	8	2	4	6	3
5	6	2	4	3	1	7	9	8
8	3	4	9	6	7	1	5	2
6	9	7	3	1	8	2	4	5
3	5	8	7	2	4	9	1	6
4	2	1	6	5	9	8	3	7
9	8	6	1	7	5	3	2	4
1	7	5	2	4	3	6	8	9
2	4	3	8	9	6	5	7	1

MIXAGRAMS

ABIDE LEFT
KAPUT ODOR
ARISE BLOB
PENAL MATH